TV GUIDE

WORD-FIND™

PUZZLES

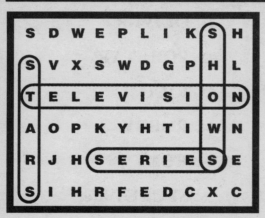

TV lovers, you'll enjoy hours of entertainment with TV Guide Word-Find™ Puzzles! Each page has lots of words about your favorite shows and stars. Your challenge is to find the UPPERCASE words in the puzzle grids and circle them. Old-time shows and new ones alike, they're all found in TV Guide Word-Finds™. So grab a pencil and turn on the fun!

Visit us!
● www.kappapuzzles.com ●

Acknowledgements

From TV Guide®:
Steve Scebelo • Karina Reeves

From Kappa Books:
• Janis Weiner • Bethany Lawler
• Denise Fulton • Joel Nanni
• Sally Andersen • Melissa Lenos
• Karen Powell • Megan Wise

VOLUME 17

 KAPPA Books
A Division of KAPPA Graphics, L.P.

"Hannah Montana"

1. BILLY RAY Cyrus	16. LOLA
2. BOOKS	17. MIKE
3. "The Best of BOTH WORLDS"	18. MILEY Stewart (character)
4. CONCERTS	19. MITCHEL Musso
5. Miley CYRUS (actress)	20. MUSICAL sitcom
6. DISNEY Channel	21. OLIVER
7. DOLLY Parton	22. POP STAR
8. EMILY Osment	23. RICO
9. FEATURE film	24. ROBBY
10. Video GAMES	25. ROXY
11. HANNAH Montana	26. SECRET life
12. Concealed IDENTITY	27. SOUNDTRACKS
13. JACKSON	28. (3-D) SPECIAL
14. JAKE RYAN	29. TEEN sensation
15. LILLY	30. World TOUR
	31. VICKI Lawrence

Word-Find 1

```
S D L R O W H T O B Y Y Q L L
T K P O P S T A R I T L O V D
R I C O Q Z P A D E H L L J S
E W H A J A K E R Y A N Y I Y
C X F B R E N C C N E X P L
N L N B M T E O I I N E O S L
O J F I I S D S S F A T R Y O
C C L T T L U N K K H L Y Y D
R Y Y E C M L X U X C E A D F
G U V R H V G Y Q O L A I M O
M X O U E I R A R I S S J Q F
S I A T L C P O M A N E M F C
M U K A K K E P A E Y B B O R
O R R E V I L O Y L S U R Y C
R D G F W V P Q S K O O B S Q
```

"Knight Rider"

1. **APRIL**
2. **ARTIFICIAL** intelligence
3. **AUTONOMIC**
4. **BONNIE**
5. **CADILLACS**
6. **CRIMEFIGHTER**
7. William **DANIELS**
8. **DEVON**
9. **F.L.A.G.**
10. David **HASSELHOFF**
11. **HIGH-TECH**
12. Rebecca **HOLDEN**
13. New **IDENTITY**
14. **KITT**
15. Patricia **MCPHERSON**
16. **MECHANIC**
17. **MICHAEL** Knight
18. Edward **MULHARE**
19. Peter **PARROS**
20. Former **POLICE** detective
21. **REGINALD** Cornelius (III)
22. Deanna **RUSSO**
23. **SECRET** organization
24. **SIDEKICK**
25. **SMART CAR**
26. **SPIN-OFFS**
27. Pontiac **TRANS-AM**

Word-Find 2

```
O  R  T  B  C  A  D  I  L  L  A  C  S  P  D
A  N  E  D  L  O  H  S  E  C  R  E  T  A  E
F  R  Y  T  I  T  N  E  D  I  C  N  N  C  M
B  L  T  B  V  Y  E  S  M  I  A  I  E  I  I
L  R  A  I  G  I  M  E  M  D  E  V  O  N  C
Z  H  E  G  F  F  O  H  L  E  S  S  A  H
A  M  C  B  B  I  N  E  S  K  S  M  L  H  A
H  C  N  E  G  O  C  M  C  R  F  A  S  C  E
L  P  M  H  T  I  N  I  A  P  F  R  N  E  L
L  H  T  U  L  H  K  N  A  S  O  T  N  M  E
E  E  A  O  L  E  G  R  I  L  N  C  D  K  K
R  R  P  S  D  H  R  I  H  E  I  A  V  I  L
Q  S  S  I  G  O  A  I  H  P  P  R  R  T  B
W  O  S  U  S  I  Q  R  U  S  S  O  P  T  Z
C  N  D  L  A  N  I  G  E  R  X  U  B  A  U
```

"Criminal Minds"

1. A. J. COOK
2. BEHAVIORAL Analysis Unit
3. Paget BREWSTER
4. COMPUTER whiz
5. Crime DRAMA
6. FBI AGENTS
7. Penelope GARCIA
8. GENIUS
9. Thomas GIBSON
10. GIDEON
11. Lola GLAUDINI
12. Elle GREENAWAY
13. Matthew Gray GUBLER
14. "HOTCH"
15. INVESTIGATE
16. JURISDICTION
17. Joe MANTEGNA
18. MOBILE organization
19. Shemar MOORE
20. Derek MORGAN
21. Mandy PATINKIN
22. Emily PRENTISS
23. PROFILERS
24. QUANTICO. Virginia
25. ROSSI
26. Fly to crime SCENE
27. Dr. SPENCER Reid
28. TEAM
29. Kirsten VANGSNESS

Word-Find 3

```
H Y T E A M G P C G I D E O N
K O O C J A O Q U A N T I C O
I E T G R N B R E W S T E R I
E N H C R G R S G T S F F N T
L Y I V H E P C N A E R V E C
I A N D C T E E I C N E H K I
B H R N U N G N L P S R R S D
O R E O F A A E A T G O E S S
M P D K I M L T I W N O T I I
S N N B A V I G R Y A M U T R
R F F R Q N A E E Z V Y P N U
K O D K K T L H N N C Z M E J
F W S I E B S R E L I F O R P
X J N S U Y D A M B Q U C P M
B E A G I B S O N W G U S X M
```

"Growing Pains" Cast

1. ALAN
2. THICKE as
3. DR. JASON
   Seaver;
4. JOANNA
5. KERNS as
6. MAGGIE Malone-
   Seaver;
7. KIRK
8. CAMERON as
9. MIKE Seaver;
10. TRACEY
11. GOLD as
12. CAROL ANNE
    Seaver;
13. JEREMY
14. MILLER as
15. BEN SEAVER;
16. ASHLEY
17. JOHNSON as
18. CHRISSY Seaver;
19. LEONARDO
20. DICAPRIO as
21. LUKE
22. BROWER Seaver;
23. JOSH ANDREW
24. KOENIG as
25. RICHARD
26. "BONER" Stabone.
27. MINOR guest
28. APPEARANCES
    were made by
29. Matthew PERRY,
30. BRAD PITT,
31. CANDACE
    Cameron,
32. HILARY Swank,
33. HEATHER
    Graham,
34. and Leah REMINI.

Word-Find 4

```
K  K  S  J  S  C  K  B  J  N  N  Y  L  N  L
E  A  C  I  N  I  M  E  R  A  N  S  O  N  U
R  S  A  A  L  Y  R  A  L  I  H  S  R  Q  K
N  H  N  O  R  E  M  A  C  B  N  I  E  Z  E
S  L  D  R  M  H  O  N  E  H  C  R  L  P  K
M  E  A  Y  E  A  Z  N  O  H  B  H  L  R  C
N  Y  C  A  N  W  S  J  A  S  R  C  I  A  I
B  V  E  N  N  E  O  R  D  R  A  K  M  E  H
J  O  S  H  A  N  D  R  E  W  D  J  T  T  T
D  Y  N  V  L  R  A  K  B  K  P  O  R  V  R
S  L  E  E  O  D  A  O  P  M  I  K  E  D  O
U  R  O  C  R  L  B  E  J  A  T  L  M  W  N
E  I  G  G  A  M  R  N  P  W  T  O  R  C  I
G  J  E  V  C  R  O  I  R  P  A  C  I  D  M
L  T  R  Y  Y  N  T  G  H  E  A  T  H  E  R
```

1. **AMERICAN** Idol
2. The **APPRENTICE**
3. **AVERAGE** Joe
4. The **BACHELOR**
5. The **BIGGEST** Loser
6. Big **BROTHER**
7. Last **COMIC** Standing
8. **DANCING** with the Stars
9. Top **DESIGN**
10. **EXTREME** Makeover
11. **FARMER** Wants a Wife
12. **FLAVOR** of Love
13. Hell's **KITCHEN**
14. **LAGUNA** Beach
15. **MADE**
16. **MIAMI INK**
17. The **MOLE**
18. (I) Love **NEW YORK**
19. What **NOT TO WEAR**
20. The **REAL WORLD**
21. **ROCK** of Love
22. Road **RULES**
23. Project **RUNWAY**
24. The **SIMPLE** Life
25. Design **STAR**
26. **SUPERNANNY**
27. The **SURREAL** Life
28. **TEMPTATION** Island
29. **THE SHOT**
30. **TOP CHEF**
31. America's Next **TOP MODEL**
32. **WIFE SWAP**

Word-Find 5

```
P D A N C I N G W G N N A P
S I M P L E E I T S E G G I B
E W E I T D F C A H U A I W M
L F R L A E I V C V P P S X B
U E I M S M M T O L E P E A R
R H C W O U I P E X R R D N O
K C A C B K R I T U R E A U T
R P N S U P E R N A N N Y G H
O O R U L F E W E K T T M A E
Y T L W D M A W A A N I X L R
W S H E E Y O R W M L C O C O
E K Z E H T O P M O D E L N V
N M C L T C T T H E S H O T A
D L R O W L A E R M R A T S L
T M N M R X N B B R P E F Y F
```

"That '70s Show"

1. ASHTON Kutcher
2. BASEMENT
3. Tommy CHONG
4. DANNY Masterson
5. DEBRA JO Rupp
6. DONNA Pinciotti
7. ERIC Forman
8. FAMILY
9. FEZ
10. FOREIGN exchange student
11. Steven HYDE
12. JACKIE Burkhart
13. Lisa Robin KELLY
14. Michael KELSO
15. KURTWOOD Smith
16. LAURA Prepon
17. LAURIE Forman
18. LEO
19. MIDGE and Bob Pinciotti
20. MILA Kunis
21. NEIGHBORS
22. RED AND KITTY Forman
23. High SCHOOL
24. Don STARK
25. "In the STREET"
26. TANYA Roberts
27. TEENAGERS
28. TOPHER Grace
29. WILMER Valderrama
30. WISCONSIN

A	Y	V	F	K	R	A	T	S	Y	L	K	X	Q	
C	M	I	L	A	U	R	I	E	B	Q	E	P	U	H
J	M	E	G	D	I	M	R	E	H	P	O	T	G	C
O	E	Y	T	T	I	K	D	N	A	D	E	R	N	G
Q	L	S	N	E	E	R	Z	A	D	O	S	L	E	K
H	A	J	C	I	E	C	Z	G	G	O	I	D	M	D
O	U	I	K	H	S	R	U	E	S	W	N	F	T	Y
E	R	C	C	D	O	N	T	R	F	T	O	N	L	M
E	A	L	R	H	E	O	O	S	R	R	W	L	A	B
J	A	E	E	W	O	B	L	C	E	U	E	K	Y	Y
E	S	D	M	T	H	N	R	I	S	K	C	L	N	D
B	H	Y	L	G	P	O	G	A	S	I	I	H	A	U
K	T	H	I	G	U	N	G	G	J	M	W	N	T	C
L	O	E	W	D	K	Q	B	U	A	O	N	E	G	Q
T	N	E	M	E	S	A	B	F	A	Y	W	I	A	D

Variety Show Hosts

1. Steve ALLEN
2. Milton BERLE
3. Carol BURNETT
4. Sid CAESAR
5. Glen CAMPBELL
6. Johnny CARSON
7. Johnny CASH
8. Imogene COCA
9. Perry COMO
10. DONNY AND MARIE
11. Judy GARLAND
12. Jackie GLEASON
13. George GOBEL
14. Arthur GODFREY
15. Danny KAYE
16. Nat KING COLE
17. Ernie KOVACS
18. Barbara MANDRELL
19. Dean MARTIN
20. The MUPPETS
21. Bob NEWHART
22. Tony ORLANDO and Dawn
23. Dolly PARTON
24. ROWAN and Martin
25. SHA NA NA
26. Frank SINATRA
27. Red SKELTON
28. The SMOTHERS Brothers
29. SONNY AND CHER
30. The STATLER Brothers
31. Ed SULLIVAN
32. Bobby VINTON
33. Porter WAGONER
34. Andy WILLIAMS

```
W A G O N E R M C A R S O N U
R N L S M O T H E R S A C O C
G A O L N A V I L L U S Q S O
M N S A E R E L O U A B S A M
G A O E Y N E L C U U S S E O
C H N J A B N C G R M Y I L Y
D S N D P C A O N A M O N G E
M N Y M R S B E I E D P A O Y
U S A E H E T L K N W M T E A
P C N L L T L A A V A H R S K
P A D R R I K L T R I F A R H
E V C E W A R M T L D N O R K
T O H B J O G I Q O E W T A T
S K E L T O N G G P A R T O N
E I R A M D N A Y N N O D P N
```

Tracee Ellis Ross

1. TRACEE
2. ELLIS
3. ROSS is
4. BEST
5. KNOWN for her
6. LEAD
7. PART as
8. JOAN
9. CLAYTON on
10. "GIRLFRIENDS,"
11. a TV SITCOM
12. THAT RAN for
13. EIGHT
14. SEASONS.
15. SHE HAS ALSO
16. STARRED in
17. SEVERAL
18. MOVIES, and was
19. A HOST for
20. "THE DISH."
21. Her FIRST
22. PUBLIC
23. APPEARANCE was as an
24. INFANT on the
25. COVER of
26. EBONY
27. MAGAZINE with her
28. FAMOUS
29. MOTHER —
30. DIANA Ross.

```
N C T G E P D E R E H T O M U
R O S S M E N A U G S I Q O H
C T O Z R I C O E H U R G C Z
D V H R Z K T A T L O U S T B
I U A A K K N D R Y M E N I T
G T G P T M T O R T A A T S K
S A K P H R O L W S F L E V N
M F C E E N A V O N C B C T M
E W I A D E E N I O T H G I E
J U L R I N S E V E R A L S B
O S L A S A H E H S S A A I O
A Q R N H T R A P U U N U L N
N H D C I L B U P K A K L L Y
S D N E I R F L R I G U K E V
A N R N P M I I D D Y R G R R
```

1. **ANIMATED** segment
2. **Sage BROCKLEBANK**
3. **BURTON "Gus"** Guster
4. **BUZZ MCNAB**
5. **CARLTON** Lassiter
6. **CHILDHOOD** memories
7. **CLUES**
8. Crime **CONSULTANT**
9. **CORBIN** Bernsen
10. **DEDUCTION**
11. **DETECTIVE**
12. **DULE HILL**
13. **FATHER**
14. **FLASHBACKS**
15. **HENRY** Spencer
16. **"I KNOW You Know"**
17. **JAMES RODAY**
18. **JULES** O'Hara
19. **KAREN** Vick
20. **KIRSTEN** Nelson
21. Maggie **LAWSON**
22. **OBSERVATION** skills
23. **PARTNERS**
24. **POLICE** department
25. Fake **PSYCHIC**
26. **SANTA** Barbara
27. **SHAWN** Spencer
28. **TIMOTHY** Omundson
29. **USA NETWORK**

Word-Find 9

```
K N A B E L K C O R B A E F N
N O S W A L Z M O Y G L V N W
T I M O T H Y D E T A M I N A
L T C S K R F C N U W J T A H
G A H H N F L A S H B A C K S
A V P E I U T A T W S M E I N
N R H B E L N J W H L E T R O
I E P S U E D P J L E S E S T
B S Q S T Z A H I L W R D T L
R B N W Y R Z H O B L O O E R
O O O H T C E M U O K D N N A
C R T N R L H R C L D A L K C
K D E D U C T I O N N Y R G I
O R S D P O L I C E A X L E A
S M A T N A S E L U J B I I N
```

"Get Smart"

1. Don ADAMS
2. AGENTS
3. Seven Emmy AWARDS
4. BARBARA Feldon
5. "Would you BELIEVE...?"
6. CATCHPHRASES
7. CHIEF
8. CONTROL
9. DISGUISES
10. EIGHTY-SIX
11. GADGETS
12. GOVERNMENT
13. HYMIE the Robot
14. INVESTIGATE
15. KAOS
16. Bernie KOPELL
17. Agent LARABEE
18. "...and LOVING IT"
19. MAXWELL Smart
20. "MISSED IT by that much"
21. MISSIONS
22. NINETY-NINE
23. Edward PLATT
24. SATIRE
25. SHOE phone
26. SIEGFRIED
27. Cone of SILENCE
28. "SORRY about that, Chief!"
29. SPIES
30. WASHINGTON, D.C.

Word-Find 10

```
C A W A R D S F R H Y M I E T
E T A G I T S E V N I R C X S
S E S A R H P H C T A C R J M
O S H Z O T N E M N R E V O G
E D I E D H S I L L E P O K S
N I N A T E S S A O C H I E F
I T G X G S I R V V S C S B P
N I T H I E A R H I O I E E L
Y D O O T B N S F N U J S L A
T E N S E Y A T T G D A E I T
E S D E M T S R S I E W I E T
N S C K I A O I B T X I P V H
I I K R A L D F X A K O S E K
N M E X N O Q A M C R F Q P W
E C N E L I S T E G D A G K Y
```

1. ALIENS in America
2. Back at the BARNYARD
3. The BIG BANG Theory
4. BIONIC Woman
5. CAVEMEN
6. CHARM School
7. CHELSEA Lately
8. CHUCK
9. DIRT
10. The Black DONNELLYS
11. DON'T FORGET the Lyrics!
12. The DRESDEN Files
13. The Bill ENGVALL Show
14. FLASH Gordon
15. FLIPPING Out
16. Shear GENIUS
17. GOSSIP Girl
18. GREEK
19. ICARLY
20. LA INK
21. LIFE IS WILD
22. Dirty Sexy MONEY
23. MOONLIGHT
24. Burn NOTICE
25. PHINEAS and Ferb
26. PUSHING Daisies
27. RULES of Engagement
28. SAMANTHA Who?
29. SAVING Grace
30. The STARTER Wife
31. Cory in THE HOUSE
32. The TUDORS

Word-Find 11

```
K C U H C T B N C P A V T E S
D L I W S I E F I L I U E C A
K B I N G Z M G I M D S D I V
E O C B O M C E R O U O S T I
E G A E Z I N V R O N N A O N
R N R C H S B S H N F E H N G
G L L A V G N E E L C T T S U
N A Y V M F H L A I U H N V A
I C F E H T L S P G G A O H
H Z H M Y Y H I S H P R M R D
S D R E S D E N P T I G A E M
U U N N L A I N K P D N S K C
P O P Y Y S E L U R I I E R Q
M W K V T W E D R A Y N R A B
G E N I U S T A R T E R G T S
```

1. **JAMES L.**
2. **BROOKS**
3. **STARTED** his
4. **TELEVISION**
5. **CAREER** as a
6. **WRITER**
7. for **CBS NEWS.**
8. He soon **SWITCHED**
9. to **FICTION**
10. and now has **NINETEEN**
11. **PRIMETIME**
12. **EMMYS** for
13. **WRITING**
14. and **PRODUCING** a
15. **WIDE**
16. **VARIETY**
17. of **SERIES**
18. such as "The

MARY
19. **TYLER**
20. **MOORE** Show,"
21. "**TAXI,**"
22. "The **TRACEY**
23. **ULLMAN** Show,"
24. and its **SPIN-OFF,**
25. "The **SIMPSONS.**"
26. He's also **PULLED OFF**
27. the **RARE**
28. **TRIPLE**
29. **OSCAR WIN**
30. as **PRODUCER,**
31. **DIRECTOR,** and writer
32. of the **BEST PICTURE**
33. "**TERMS** of
34. **ENDEARMENT.**"

Word-Find 12

```
E N T R I P L E M M Y S P R A
R E T N N O I S I V E L E T D
U E R S E R I E S M S L R E S
T T R M S M A M I E Y O T W H
C E O O P W R T M T T R Q W E
I N W S O E E A N C A F A F F
P I O R T M J N E T X F F M C
T N P W I X N R S D I O B A S
S I W R D T I A A B N D R S U
E W P I O D I M M I C E O T L
B R K T D D H N P L E L O R W
B A A E M E U S G R L L K A L
E C P R O D U C I N G U S C U
M S S W I T C H E D Z P I E L
N O I T C I F V A R I E T Y K
```

"That Was the Week That Was"

1. ALAN Alda
2. Tom BOSLEY
3. BUCK Henry
4. BURR Tillstrom
5. CABARET
6. DAVID Frost
7. Bob DISHY
8. ELLIOT Reid
9. Pat ENGLUND
10. Stanley GROVER
11. HENRY Morgan
12. IMPROV
13. JERRY Damon
14. Tom LEHRER
15. LIVE
16. Doro MERANDE
17. MUSICAL
   numbers

18. NANCY Ames
19. NEWS reports
20. NICKNAMED
   (TW3)
21. ORCHESTRA
22. Norman PARIS
23. PHYLLIS Newman
24. PIONEER show
25. POKED fun
26. POLITICAL
27. PUPPETS
28. REGULARS
29. SANDY Baron
30. SATIRE
31. Ned SHERRIN
32. SKETCHES

Word-Find 13

```
U W K E D E M A N K C I N P Q
Y D N A S B U R R B L P O I G
O A W N Y O I T O I L L E O Y
S K E T C H E S V C I E W N I
K R V N N P I E V T G H D E K
E Y E E A L V H I K H R N E P
R D W G L L P C P C H E U R D
I S N Y U A A R G U Y R L F I
T M H A Y L E O T B P R G W V
A P P R R V A E D S B P N U A
S D R R O E R R S O O B E E D
W E I R O A M U S I C A L T H
J K G S B V S L N I R R E H S
W O D A H F E P V N F A Z T A
D P C H W Y C N A N M Q P N K
```

1. LLOYD
2. BRIDGES
3. HAD HIS OWN
4. EPONYMOUS
5. SHOW, as well as
6. the EXTREMELY
7. POPULAR
8. "SEA HUNT."
9. His TWO SONS —
10. BEAU and
11. JEFF —
12. APPEARED on it
13. as CHILDREN.
14. LATER,
15. Beau and Jeff CO-HOSTED
16. "SATURDAY
17. NIGHT
18. LIVE."
19. Beau's SERIES
20. INCLUDE
21. "ENSIGN
22. O'TOOLE,"
23. "MAXIMUM Bob,"
24. "The AGENCY,"
25. and "STARGATE (SG-1)."
26. His FATHER
27. STARRED with him
28. in "HARTS OF
29. THE WEST."
30. JORDAN Bridges,
31. Beau's SON, WAS
32. a REGULAR
33. in "DAWSON'S Creek"
34. and "CONVICTION."

Word-Find 14

```
N G I S N E S N O S O W T R S
O W O J V S M A X I M U M X A
I H O I D C D N T S H O W G W
T T L S D A E T N U H A E S N
C S H J I R W R Y O R N O J O
I E L G D H A S B M C D E V S
V W R L I L D R O Y D F A E N
N E I A U N I A A N F A X Y G
O H H P L D C O H O S T E D C
C T O P G U N L S P R H J E C
G P G E J A G T U E O E X R D
F U S A D P R E M D I R T R Y
S T A R G A T E R H E R J A O
Y L O E H E L O O T O Y E T L
G J D D B Y M G M F G A A S L
```

Title Characters

1. Captain **BARNEY** Miller
2. **BETTY** Suarez
3. Dr. "**BONES**" Brennan
4. **CHRISTINE** Campbell
5. **DEXTER** Morgan
6. **EARL** Hickey
7. **FRASIER** Crane
8. **GEORGE** Lopez
9. **GRACE** Adler
10. **HANNAH** Montana
11. Colonel Robert **HOGAN**
12. Dr. Gregory **HOUSE**
13. **JOAN GIRARDI**
14. **LAVERNE** De Fazio
15. **LUCY** Ricardo
16. **MALCOLM**
17. **MINDY** McConnell
18. **MORK**
19. **PERRY** Mason
20. **RAYMOND** Barone
21. **REBA** Hart
22. Jerry **SEINFELD**
23. **SHIRLEY** Feeney
24. Eli **STONE**
25. Will **TRUMAN**
26. **VERONICA** Mars
27. Cordell **WALKER**

Word-Find 15

```
D I V G S U C Q G R I D V U N
N Y E L R I H S J E R D R W X
K R O M J B B H L B H E E X H
W V Y W C O O O S A L X I Z Z
P M R R P U A E D V V T S E X
C H R I S T I N E J W E A H C
E G E E G N O H G T L R R M P
G E P J F M A F Y I L R F N V
R M N E Y F H M B A R N E Y E
O W L A N G D O U E C A R G R
E D R O S O N R G R T N R E O
G O U Q C E T C M A T T K D N
L T U P S L O S E N N L Y P I
E N H A N N A H D G A F X R C
L U C Y D N I M R W D S U E A
```

TV GUIDE

"The Daily Show"

1. CREATED

2. by LIZZ

3. WINSTEAD

4. and MADELEINE

5. SMITHBERG,

6. "THE DAILY

7. SHOW"

8. WAS A

9. MODEST

10. HIT ON

11. COMEDY

12. CENTRAL,

13. UNTIL

14. HOST

15. CRAIG

16. KILBORN

17. LEFT.

18. ONCE

19. JON STEWART

20. TOOK

21. OVER

22. the FAUX

23. ANCHOR

24. DESK,

25. BOTH

26. CRITICAL

27. ACCLAIM

28. and RATINGS

29. SOARED.

30. The show HAS WON

31. two PEABODY

32. and ten EMMY

33. AWARDS.

Word-Find 16

```
S M M Y L I A D E H T L L S U
W G A F E D C L M S S T I B L
V L D U W A A I O H O A T Z V
Y D E S K C W E R O H C N A Z
I D L F I I S A T W J C U R J
J C E T T O L O R S Y L V E J
H O I M A U O B C D N A N V U
R R N R O K X E O K S I O O S
C Q E S V C N B D R H M W L X
G D G H T T A K E I N W S U H
I I O G R E B H T I M S A P H
X G A A P G W O A F U F H S X
N V L R R H N A E M M Y Q X A
K N O N C E U E R A T I N G S
S J H Y H T O B C T S E D O M
```

Marlee Matlin

1. Best ACTRESS awards
2. "ASKART"
3. AUTHOR
4. "BLUES Clues"
5. "BRIDGE to Silence"
6. Involved with CHARITY
7. "Freak CITY"
8. "DANCING with the Stars"
9. "DEAD Silence"
10. "In Her DEFENSE"
11. "Reasonable DOUBTS"
12. FOUR KIDS
13. HEARING impaired
14. ILLINOIS
15. "KISS My Act"
16. "Children of a LESSER God"
17. "The L WORD"
18. MARRIED
19. "Hear NO EVIL"
20. OSCAR
21. "It's My PARTY"
22. "PICKET Fences"
23. "The PLAYER"
24. PRODUCER
25. "Two SHADES of Blue"
26. "SNITCH"
27. STAGE
28. "SWEET Nothing in My Ear"
29. "WALKER"
30. "The WEST Wing"

Word-Find 17

```
C R M S T A G E B J Q N I O W
R E C U D O R P I C K E T L X
E Z Q G N I R O H T U A P L A
S K I S S L K A O S C A R S O
S H R W N L R R C S R S K I A
E D E E X I I R U T H A S T G
L L K A T N T V Y O R T K X U
W X L Y R O K C E T F E X D H
O M A T H I E S H O L H S R E
R A W I S S N R E X N H T S G
D R G C N W E G L U A A G G D
D R F E D Y E I W D L D Y W I
C I F Z A T N E E I C B A D R
K E W L F V S S T B U O D E B
D D P J A T X K G N I C N A D
```

George Gobel

1. AFTER his
2. TV DEBUT on
3. "The COLGATE
4. COMEDY Hour"
5. and GUEST
6. SPOTS
7. with DINAH Shore,
8. PERRY Como,
9. STEVE Allen, and
    more,
10. George GOBEL got
11. his own
    EPONYMOUS
12. SERIES for which
13. he EARNED an
14. EMMY and
15. a PEABODY.
16. "LONESOME
17. GEORGE"
18. was a REGULAR
19. on "HOLLYWOOD
20. SQUARES"
21. and "HARPER
22. VALLEY PTA".
23. His QUICK wit had
24. JOHNNY
25. CARSON,
26. Dean MARTIN,
27. and BOB HOPE in
28. HYSTERICS on
29. "The TONIGHT
    Show"
30. when he ASKED,
    "Do you
31. EVER FEEL
32. THAT LIFE is a
33. TUXEDO and
    you're
34. a pair of BROWN
35. SHOES?"

Word-Find 18

```
T H G I N O T R E P R A H I P
A S N D T U B E D V T D K M J
N R E P E R R Y H P E E C A G
C F E U N N R N Y K N G I G V
E O C G G V R E S S O R U T Q
S M L S U L L A T E S O Q P O
H T O G E L L E E F R E V E O
C O E S A I A N R I A G S A Y
O O L V E T R R I L C Q E B J
M G F L E N E E C T U P M O A
E P O N Y M O U S A O A H D S
D N V B Q W G L R H R N I Y P
Y T U X E D O E B T N N Q M O
M U M C S L S O I Y A P X M T
I S N W O R B N D H S H O E S
```

1. "Great SCOTT"

2. FEATURED

3. a TEENAGE

4. TOBEY

5. MAGUIRE

6. and KEVIN

7. CONNOLLY of

8. "ENTOURAGE"

9. in HIGH

10. SCHOOL

11. ANGST.

12. "The Great

DEFENDER"

13. STARRED

14. MICHAEL Rispoli,

from

15. "The

SOPRANOS,"

16. as a STREET

17. SMART

18. BOSTON

19. LAWYER.

20. The SELF-

21. EXPLANATORY

22. "Great CIRCUSES

23. OF THE

24. WORLD"

25. was HOSTED

26. BY MARY

27. HART

28. FROM "ET."

Word-Find 19

```
D G M S O P R A N O S H D A R
F T P I E V E T C C E L I L E
R Y P G C S X T E E R T S G E
N D R L T H U G T O B E Y X H
I S M A R T A C W I X Y P K A
V K L W M N O E R S E L F F R
E A F Y E Y S C L I A L R E T
K N W E R C B E S N C O D N R
I O T R H S T H A L M N A O J
H U K O P T U T B E E N A T N
U O O B U A O F T F G O L S L
Y L S Z T R K O E S M C E O W
L T W T Y R A D T U Y P I B M
P N F Z E E B G E R I U G A M
T B J J M D D D E R U T A E F
```

Estelle Getty

1. As ESTELLE
2. GETTY
3. PUT IT,
4. AFTER
5. FORTY
6. YEARS of
7. ACTING,
8. she BECAME
9. "an OVERNIGHT
10. SUCCESS at
11. THE AGE of
12. SIXTY-TWO"
13. on "GOLDEN
14. GIRLS".
15. She PLAYED
16. SOPHIA
17. PETRILLO,
18. the MOTHER of
19. BEATRICE
20. ARTHUR, who was
21. ACTUALLY
22. FIFTEEN
23. MONTHS
24. OLDER than
    Estelle.
25. SHE DID
26. GUEST
27. APPEARANCES
28. as Sophia on
    "EMPTY NEST",
29. "NURSES",
30. and BLOSSOM."
31. SHE WON a
32. Golden GLOBE
    and an
33. EMMY as Sophia.

Word-Find 20

```
X R A O E Y K D I D E H S Q K
B E C A M E Z Y M M E E G L T
L D T C S U C C E S S Y D T I
O L I N L E M E M R H T A S T
S O N O B S C O U U S H F L U
S S G O J I N N T R K G T T P
O L L I R T E P A H Z I E I N
M G J T H M A E O R E N R O C
N C A S S R Y C W S A R W T J
P E L I T E M P T Y N E S T T
B J E H H S U E Y U H V P T H
Y J U T H P L G T S A O H P E
Q R M P F L O R X N U L U O A
L W I X E I S S I N E D L O G
L P Y T R O F J S G E T T Y E
```

Adam Baldwin's Credits

1. ABOVE & Beyond
2. ANGEL
3. BETRAYAL
4. BLIND Justice
5. Day BREAK
6. The CAPE
7. Jackie CHAN Adventures
8. CHUCK
9. CRUEL Doubt
10. DRILLBIT Taylor
11. DR. JEKYLL and Mr. Hyde
12. EVIL Eyes
13. Control FACTOR
14. FIREFLY
15. The FREEDIVER
16. FULL Metal Jacket
17. HYPER Sonic
18. INDEPENDENCE Day
19. The INSIDE
20. JACKPOT
21. MURDER in High Places
22. The PATRIOT
23. Ordinary PEOPLE
24. The POSEIDON Adventure
25. PREDATOR 2
26. RADIO Flyer
27. SANDS of Oblivion
28. SERENITY
29. SMOKE Jumpers
30. TALK to Me
31. The THIRST
32. From the Earth TO THE MOON
33. The VISITOR
34. WYATT Earp
35. The X-FILES

Word-Find 21

```
R M D M N S L X P A T R I O T
E P R E D A T O R E B L I L Y
D J X N S S S E A E O O I J L
R R A F M E V S D U P P V V F
U S Q O I I R J I C M Y L E E
M G K D D L B E O R D S H E R
V E O E C N E D N E P E D N I
D N E A D D T S O I D J D A F
L R P M I Z R J O O T N R H V
F E J S L O A K M I P Y I C R
B K N E T C Y L E U R C L L C
R I G C K D A C H U C K L Y B
E N A P F Y L T T A Y W B V U
A F O F U L L R O T I S I V T
K T H I R S T L T K L A T O W
```

Lucille Ball

1. ACTRESS
2. Desi ARNAZ
3. Lucy BARKER
4. Diane BELMONT (early stage name)
5. BIT PLAYER
6. Lucy CARMICHAEL
7. Lucy CARTER
8. COMEDIENNE
9. "CRITIC'S Choice"
10. DANCER
11. DESILU Studios
12. EMMY Awards
13. "FANCY Pants"
14. FIASCOES
15. GOLDEN Globes
16. GOLDWYN Girl
17. Gale GORDON
18. "HERE'S Lucy"
19. "My Favorite HUSBAND"
20. "I LOVE LUCY"
21. Buster KEATON
22. "LIFE with Lucy"
23. "MAME"
24. QUEEN of comedy
25. REDHEAD
26. Lucy RICARDO
27. SCHEMES
28. "The Lucy SHOW"
29. SITCOMS
30. SLAPSTICK
31. "STONE Pillow"
32. TELEVISION
33. "The Long, Long TRAILER"
34. ZIEGFELD girl

Word-Find 22

```
D C N E D L O G N O T A E K F
N A A T G N G O L D W Y N A G
O C E R E Y A L P T I B N R O
D T B H T L C B I R E C E N B
R R S S D E E M S M Y K I A H
O E C M L E R V A U Z K D Z O
G S H O C A R M I C H A E L D
Q S E C E U P L T S F Z M K Q
M S M T L X O S R R I S O I D
R E E I L V C E T E A O C Q A
Q R S S E I K Y G I S I N U N
U E M L T R F F M K C T L E C
D H U I A K E E T M O K O E E
S C R B E L M O N T E I W N R
Y C F O D R A C I R S H O W E
```

"Parental Control"

1. MTV'S
2. "PARENTAL
3. CONTROL"
4. PUTS A
5. UNIQUE
6. SPIN ON
7. "THE DATING
8. GAME."
9. PARENTS
10. WHO DON'T
11. LIKE
12. THEIR
13. TEENAGE
14. CHILD'S
15. PARTNER
16. INTERVIEW
17. a HANDFUL
18. of POSSIBLE
19. NEW ONES.
20. FATHER
21. and MOTHER
22. EACH
23. SELECT
24. HIS OR HER
25. FAVORITE
26. CANDIDATE,
27. who THEN
28. GOES OUT
29. with their OFFSPRING.
30. The DATER
31. then CHOOSES
32. BETWEEN the
33. CURRENT date, or
34. ONE CHOSEN
35. BY THE parents.

Word-Find 23

```
S F H G N E E G A N E E T T D
R J Q O W H M Z B E T W E E N
C I O E R E T A D S P A T U O
O F F S P R I N G O C K R Q N
N B V O E F S V S H R N E I I
T Y K U A T N S R C I E H N P
R T S T N C I T U E U W R U S
O H H E H B H R T N T O O N R
L E R I L E R A O O N N S Z E
R A L E I E D E N V A E I Z H
P D K R N I C A N D A S H B T
S I H T D G H T T F F T T O
L A T N E R A P V I R U A U M
A N A T N O D O H W N A L F P
D C H O O S E S V T M G P G M
```

1. BEYOND Belief
2. CELEBRITY Paranormal Project
3. America's Psychic CHALLENGE
4. CHARMED
5. CROSSING Over with John Edward
6. DARK Shadows
7. The DEAD ZONE
8. Psychic DETECTIVE
9. ENIGMA
10. GHOST Hunters International
11. American GOTHIC
12. INVASION
13. Fear ITSELF
14. Quantum LEAP
15. LOST
16. MEDIUM
17. MOST Haunted
18. MTV'S FEAR
19. NIGHTSTALKER
20. PSYCHIC Kids
21. SUPERNATURAL
22. THRESHOLD
23. TRUTH or Scare
24. UFO HUNTERS
25. UNSOLVED Mysteries
26. Ghost WHISPERER
27. The X-FILES

Word-Find 24

```
O N Y S N C V T R U T H E Z X
C O O V Z O I A S S V G W H N
S H L I Y C E H O O D G Y F D
E X A X S F W H C E M T L J A
L K R L S A G G T Y I E P C O
I D U V L A V E O R S B A R C
F E T F V E C N B T E P E E R
X M A R O T N E I Y H N L R O
O R N T I H L G O G I I W E S
M A R V S E U N E G U T C P S
E H E F C O D N M L A N T S I
D C P R E K L A T S T H G I N
I P U M D L O H S E R H T H G
U N S O L V E D Q K R A D W F
M V C E N O Z D A E D S G C I
```

1. **MARISKA**
2. **HARGITAY**
3. **is WELL-KNOWN**
4. **as DETECTIVE**
5. **OLIVIA**
6. **BENSON on**
7. **"Law & ORDER:**
8. **SPECIAL**
9. **VICTIMS Unit."**
10. **She won an EMMY**
11. **and a GOLDEN Globe**
12. **for this ROLE.**
13. **She's been a CAST**
14. **MEMBER**
15. **of "DOWNTOWN,"**
16. **"FALCON**
17. **CREST,"**
18. **"TEQUILA and**
19. **BONETTI,"**
20. **"CAN'T HURRY**
21. **LOVE,"**
22. **"PRINCE**
23. **STREET,"**
24. **AND "ER."**
25. **She's been a GUEST**
26. **on "THE VIEW,"**
27. **"The TONIGHT show,"**
28. **"ELLEN,"**
29. **"BAYWATCH",**
30. **and "SEINFELD".**
31. **She is the DAUGHTER**
32. **of ACTRESS**
33. **Jayne MANSFIELD**
34. **and BODYBUILDER**
35. **MICKEY Hargitay.**

```
T R E B M E M A I V I L O O E
N E L L E M M Y G O L D E N O
G D D L E I F S N A M B O W B
S R S E I N F E L D A C V O O
D O W N T O W N Q Y L K D N N
P R I N C E K L W A A Y S K E
C R B R A P C A F Y B N W L T
A T E X N Z T T A U E E D L T
S S N T T C S T I K I K S E I
T M S U H E I L O V S P C W R
R I O E U G D D E N E I D I E
E T N G R E U H S C I V R L M
E C A A R T T A I X A G O A T
T I H X Y H C A D Y X R H L M
V V N G Y A L A L I U Q E T H
```

"Captain Midnight" Narration

1. "On a MOUNTAINTOP

2. HIGH

3. ABOVE a

4. LARGE

5. CITY

6. STANDS the

7. HEADQUARTERS

8. of a MAN

9. DEVOTED to the

10. CAUSE of

11. FREEDOM and

12. JUSTICE, a

13. WAR HERO

14. WHO HAS

15. NEVER

16. STOPPED

17. FIGHTING

18. AGAINST his

19. COUNTRY'S

20. ENEMIES, a

21. PRIVATE

22. CITIZEN

23. WHO IS

24. DEDICATING

25. his LIFE to

26. the STRUGGLE

27. against EVIL

28. men EVERYWHERE —

29. CAPTAIN

30. MIDNIGHT."

Word-Find 26

```
E R E H W Y R E V E S I O H W
S G S N F E T A V I R P O A F
W D G T L R G E N E M I E S T
H K N N O A E C L P V F E H X
O E I A I P I E E G I I G T E
H C A N T T P L D L G I L S A
A I S D I S H E E O N U U Y P
S T H Z Q T J G D D M A R R O
T Y E D N U R W I B C R N T L
Z N L E S A A M C F H M I N S
R I I T L O M R A J G N A U P
E N I O M O U N T A I N T O P
V C E V O B A B I E H U P C C
E O R E H R A W N J R A A T X
N E E D S W Z U G B O S C R L
```

"My Boys"

1. ANDY	17. P.J. FRANKLIN
2. BOBBY	18. POKER
3. BRENDAN	19. RADIO DJ
4. BROTHER	20. REID Scott
5. Michael BUNIN	21. SINGLE
6. CHICAGO	22. SITCOM
7. COLUMNIST	23. SPORTS
8. Ball FIELD	24. STEPHANIE
9. FRIENDS	25. Kellee STEWART
10. Jim GAFFIGAN	26. TAVERN
11. One of the GUYS	27. TBS NETWORK
12. JAMIE Kaler	28. Chicago Sun-
13. JORDANA Spiro	TIMES
14. KENNY	29. TOMBOY
15. KYLE Howard	30. WRITER
16. MIKE	

```
W F S M H Q X U W J D X M G S
N I L K N A R F J P W Y V D X
W D Y R S G M T C D N I N U B
I L D O Q O R O N W O E Y Y R
E V N W C A L S N A I I E J E
Y E A T W U O S Y R D I D C T
O M I E M I K E F U M N X A I
B S T N A G I F F A G O E X R
M S I S A K S Z J J J S D R W
O S S B C H I C A G O E L E B
T M P T P P P K L C R B E H L
Q W N O R L H E E K D O I T S
V M K N R E V A T N A B F O E
V E P H P T I M E S N B E R Y
R E L G N I S D F B A Y D B E
```

1. Hal HOLBROOK
2. STARTED in
3. TELEVISION on
4. the SOAP
5. OPERA
6. "The BRIGHTER

   Day."
7. SINCE
8. THEN,
9. he's WON FIVE
10. EMMYS from
11. TWELVE
12. NOMINATIONS.
13. ONE WIN was for
14. "MARK TWAIN
15. TONIGHT!," a

16. PROGRAM he
17. WROTE and
18. STARRED in.
19. It also won a

    TONY.
20. He was a CAST
21. MEMBER
22. of "EVENING
23. SHADE,"
24. APPEARED often
25. on "DESIGNING
26. WOMEN"
27. with his WIFE,
28. DIXIE
29. CARTER.

```
E D A H S N E F I W S Y P P M
R E Z C R H T T B N N D F R W
I S S T R N J K O O R B L O H
A I Q Q W E E I T R D J N G Q
R G P T E E T H A U W F T R O
T N A H C A L R T V I S T A E
T I O G N B E V A V A R P M A
U N S I I X R S E C B P M E S
Q G M N S R F I T O E Y D T J
V O G O Y I A S G A S V A E O
N J I T J R V Q R H R R V I N
G N I N E V E E P A T R N X E
X N X P D O D E L E J E E I W
Q W O M E N P W D E B N R D I
J R E B M E M A R K T W A I N
```

"In the House" Cast

ACTOR	ROLE
1. **ALFONSO** Ribeiro	1. **MAXWELL** Stanton
2. **DEBBIE** Allen	2. Jackie **WARREN**
3. **DEE JAY** Daniels	3. **RODNEY**
4. **DEREK** McGrath	4. **BERNIE**
5. **GABRIELLE** Carmouche	5. **RAYNELLE**
6. Jeffery **WOOD**	6. **AUSTIN** Warren
7. **JOHN** Amos	7. **COACH** Sam Wilson
8. Ken **LAWSON**	8. **CARL**
9. Kim **WAYANS**	9. **TONIA** Harris
10. **LARK** Voorhees	10. **MERCEDES** Langford
11. Lisa **ARRINDELL**	11. **HEATHER** Comstock
12. **LL COOL J**	12. **MARION** Hill
13. **MAIA** Campbell	13. **TIFFANY** Warren
14. **PAULETTE** Braxton	14. Natalie **DAVIS**

Word-Find 29

```
H C A O C T W W V K V R N C N
O E K J C R T M W O R Y N Y V
V M E R C E D E S Y R O X E L
R A R L J I S Q A U S T I N W
S R E Q L N A J W W C M E D L
O I D D A E E Y A A A K R O C
X O G Y G E N L A I R L A R K
P N A C D A I Y A P N R V H H
M W B L F A P B A T L O E G R
A V R F F C V U B R B N T N E
X A I N A O L I B E R N I E H
W T E R Y E N C S X D Q N X T
E S L W T M D S V K K O H E A
L W L T C J L O O C L L O D E
L L E D N I R R A U O Q J W H
```

Longest Running U.S. Shows

1. **AMERICAN Bandstand**
2. **ANOTHER World**
3. **All My CHILDREN**
4. **700 CLUB**
5. **(CBS) EVENING News**
6. **FACE the Nation**
7. **GENERAL Hospital**
8. **GOOD Morning America**
9. **GUIDING Light**
10. **HALLMARK Hall of Fame**
11. **Days of our LIVES**
12. **MASTERPIECE Theatre**
13. **MEET the Press**
14. **60 MINUTES**
15. **MISTER Rogers' Neighborhood**
16. **(NBC) NIGHTLY News**
17. **NOVA**
18. **ONE LIFE to Live**
19. **The Joy of PAINTING**
20. **Hour of POWER**
21. **The PRICE Is Right**
22. **ROMPER Room**
23. **SATURDAY Night Live**
24. **SEARCH for Tomorrow**
25. **SESAME Street**
26. **SOUL Train**
27. **Wide World of SPORTS**
28. **TODAY**
29. **The TONIGHT Show**
30. **As the World TURNS**
31. **WORLD News**
32. **The YOUNG and the Restless**

```
L E J M D B R Z C B S J N N A
A A A A I O U D H T J E S H Y
R F V J M S O I I C U A V L J
E O S P F A T G L L T R T I D
N R E W O P S E D U U H N B L
E R A Q R G G T R B G G T S R
G J R I N N C D E I X N E T O
F A C E I M A P N R F I E R W
R E H N V Y I C L D P D M O M
V E E L A N G N I T N I A P O
Z V H D T M L K U R R U E S G
E S O T H G I N O T E G L C U
Q T O F O S E S A M E M K K E
M W B U O N E L I F E S A W V
K R A M L L A H G N U O Y U P
```

1. **BEFORE**
2. **ACTING,**
3. Katey was a **BACKUP**
4. **SINGER** for
5. **BETTE**
6. **MIDLER** and
7. **TANYA**
8. **TUCKER.**
9. She's **SYNONYMOUS**
10. with Peg **BUNDY,**
11. the **CHARACTER**
12. she **RECEIVED**
13. 4 **GOLDEN**
14. **GLOBE**
15. **NOMINATIONS**
16. for **PLAYING**
17. on "**MARRIED**
18. with **CHILDREN**".
19. She's the **VOICE**
20. of **TURANGA**
21. **LEELA**
22. on "**FUTURAMA**" and
23. **CO-STARRED** on
24. "8 **SIMPLE**
25. **RULES**
26. for **DATING** my
27. **TEENAGE**
28. **DAUGHTER**".
29. Her **SISTERS** were
30. the **DOUBLEMINT**
31. **TWINS**
32. in the **CHEWING**
33. gum **COMMERCIALS.**

```
E F I S C H E W I N G D T W M
R J V I G O L D E N E A B I T
A U P S N H S T W I N S D N R
T M L T G O M T R Y B L I E E
E I A E A I M R A A E M V R T
B V Y R S L A I C R E M M O C
O U I S U M E K N L R B E F A
L E N N O T U A B A E E R E R
G L G D M P U U G T T E D B A
E P C A Y G O F T N C I L O H
C M V T N D K E D E A H O A C
I I Y I O E C H I L D R E N H
O S T N N H E V R E K C U T S
V C Y G Y R E T H G U A D T Y
A O R J S D K L R E G N I S H
```

One Word '70s TV Shows

1. ALICE
2. ANGIE
3. ARNIE
4. BARETTA
5. BEWITCHED
6. BONANZA
7. CHASE
8. CHER
9. CHIPS
10. DALLAS
11. DIANA
12. EMERGENCY
13. FAMILY
14. FISH
15. GUNSMOKE
16. IRONSIDE
17. JULIA
18. KOJAK
19. LASSIE
20. LIFELINE

21. MANNIX
22. MARY
23. M*A*S*H
24. MAUDE
25. NAKIA
26. NANCY
27. PARIS
28. PEOPLE
29. PHYLLIS
30. RHODA
31. SARGE
32. SERPICO
33. SHIRLEY
34. SIERRA
35. SOAP
36. SWITCH
37. TAXI
38. VEGAS

Word-Find 32

```
J P S E T B Z A C X H S A M L
M I I K V I F H R U I Q O Y C
O M E O G E A B O N A N Z A C
Y J R M L S G N C E I G N A P
K U R S E S I A A T T E R A B
C L A N I R O N S I D E T E M
L I Y U A S G O J I D C W D E
F A V G W H C E X E L I A U L
U T S I Z I Z A N M T L D A P
V V T S P R T I A C L A Y M O
P C P R I L L R H A Y A R H E
H A E G Q E Y E S P I H C F P
S S R J F Y D H K K O J A K G
I Y L I M A F C A D E G R A S
F J L B S C A N A N C Y Y Z R
```

Two Word '70s TV Shows

1. ADAM'S Rib
2. Charlie's ANGELS
3. Dan AUGUST
4. BORN Free
5. CADE'S County
6. Medical CENTER
7. Happy DAYS
8. FAMILY Affair
9. Silent FORCE
10. GHOST Story
11. That GIRL
12. GOOD Times
13. Lou GRANT
14. GREEN Acres
15. HEE HAW
16. HOGAN'S Heroes
17. Barnaby JONES
18. KUNG FU

19. LOGAN'S Run
20. LOVE Story
21. LUCAS Tanner
22. Lotsa LUCK
23. Here's LUCY
24. MATT Lincoln
25. MOVIN' On
26. NIGHT Gallery
27. PAPER Chase
28. Police STORY
29. THREE'S Company
30. Oregon TRAIL
31. WHITE Shadow
32. WILD Kingdom
33. Police WOMAN

Word-Find 33

```
Q O X Y G W H R B O R N E S D
D W C N E Z Y X K O E K E S X
F U H R Z A I G T U T X Q T K
L O W A H E E H J O N E S T O
G G R A N T R O T Q E G S A E
R R V C I E C S O N C U F M T
P E U H E A T T K Q G Q S U M
U E W S D G I R L U Y R O T S
Y N N E N S F F A M I L Y P U
J S S E I A G X N I O F U W A
S W Z V G C G U G R L V O C L
U M I O H U O O E N A M I X K
Z M A L T L O P L W A L I N P
S Y A D D D A I S N A G O H D
E O D S A P V U I T C A S R J
```

Cult Favorites

1. **ABSOLUTELY** Fabulous
2. The **AVENGERS**
3. **BABYLON 5**
4. **BATTLESTAR** Galactica
5. **BEAUTY** and the Beast
6. **BUFFY** the Vampire Slayer
7. **DOCTOR** Who
8. **FAMILY** Guy
9. **FARSCAPE**
10. **FIREFLY**
11. **FREAKS** and Geeks
12. Mary **HARTMAN,** Mary Hartman
13. **JERICHO**
14. **LOST**
15. Veronica **MARS**
16. **MYSTERY** Science Theater
17. Pee-Wee's **PLAYHOUSE**
18. The **PRISONER**
19. Monty **PYTHON'S** Flying Circus
20. The **SIMPSONS**
21. **STARGATE (SG-1)**
22. **STRANGERS** with Candy
23. Star **TREK**
24. **TWILIGHT** Zone
25. **TWIN** Peaks
26. **XENA:** Warrior Princess

Word-Find 34

```
Z V G Y M D Z B O N K K K I B
V F I R E F L Y H H I O E B P
Z P N E Y M A R S N C W R Y R
N S W T Y L T R A J Y I T K K
O T S S I K E M S R J H R B T
L A B Y P G T T Y C O T G E L
Y R M M N R W L U N A T J S J
B G W A A I I N S L R P C U L
A A R H L M Y S S J O J E O F
B T Y I A E T W O O T S S H D
S E G F G T U S G N J T B Y X
Y H T R F B A T T L E S T A R
T A B I D U E S K A E R F L B
V K A H L Y B P E A N E X P F
S N O S P M I S R E G N E V A
```

Nancy Marchand

1. **NANCY**
2. **MARCHAND'S**
3. **TELEVISION**
4. **DEBUT** was as the
5. **LEADING**
6. **LADY** on
7. **"MARTY."**
8. She was a **GUEST** on
9. **"PLAYHOUSE 90,"**
10. **"STUDIO ONE,"**
11. **"The DEFENDERS,"**
12. and **"CHEERS."**
13. Her **SERIES**
14. **INCLUDED**
15. **"The EDGE**
16. of **NIGHT,"**
17. **"LOVE OF LIFE,"**
18. **"ANOTHER**
19. **WORLD,"**
20. **"BEACON HILL,"**
21. **"LOVERS and**
22. **FRIENDS,"**
23. and **"FOR RICHER,**
24. **FOR POORER."**
25. Her most **POPULAR**
26. **ROLE** was as
27. **MARGARET**
28. **PYNCHON** on
29. **"LOU GRANT,"**
30. Her **LATEST**
31. was as **LIVIA**
32. on **"The SOPRANOS."**

Word-Find 35

```
E  F  I  L  F  O  E  V  O  L  A  T  E  S  T
Y  N  C  L  Q  S  M  R  A  L  U  P  O  P  N
D  T  O  I  A  P  E  Y  C  N  A  N  I  J  Z
A  R  E  H  C  I  R  R  O  F  A  I  N  P  U
L  O  C  N  C  B  V  I  I  R  A  G  C  I  S
O  E  L  O  R  N  S  I  P  E  L  H  L  T  E
U  S  M  C  F  I  Y  O  L  E  S  T  U  G  G
G  T  R  A  V  O  S  P  A  S  Y  D  D  U  P
R  S  U  E  R  I  R  D  Y  N  I  E  E  Z  S
A  R  L  B  D  T  I  P  H  O  O  S  D  S  D
N  E  R  L  E  N  Y  A  O  L  T  T  N  R  N
T  V  R  O  G  D  E  N  U  O  E  U  H  E  E
J  O  L  J  V  O  E  F  S  L  R  C  U  E  I
W  L  M  A  R  G  A  R  E  T  O  E  B  H  R
P  M  M  A  R  C  H  A  N  D  S  I  R  C  F
```

"The Big Bang Theory"

1. THIS NEW
2. SITCOM will
3. START its
4. SECOND
5. SEASON in
6. FALL 2008.
7. The SERIES
8. FOLLOWS
9. a GROUP
10. of SOCIALLY
11. INEPT,
12. SCIENCE
13. GENIUSES and
14. their BEAUTIFUL,
15. less than SMART,
16. FEMALE
17. NEIGHBOR.
18. KALEY
19. CUOCO, from
20. "8 SIMPLE
21. RULES…,"
22. STARS as the
23. GIRL
24. NEXT DOOR
25. PENNY, and
26. JOHNNY
27. GALECKI, from
28. "ROSEANNE,"
29. PLAYS one of the
30. BRAINIACS,
31. LEONARD.
32. SARA
33. GILBERT,
34. ALSO from
    "Roseanne,"
35. APPEARS as
36. LESLIE,
37. a PHYSICIST.

Word-Find 36

```
Y A J G E N I U S E S N R T P
S B P T H I K C E L A G O W U
R I L P S S A R Y F C U O C O
A U T M E I T L O Y Z F D O R
T N A C N A C A S S N E T R G
S R O I O S R I R O E M X D G
T N A D A M W S S T I A E R I
D R F R R L C O F Y G L N A L
B E A U T I F U L S H E Y N B
E I L S E L J L E L B P E O E
P E L N E O A A M H O G L E R
S Y C T H I S N E W R F A L T
M E N N C O R T P E N I K R Y
Y I N O N O P E N N Y O G I H
D Y S E L P M I S Y A L P G L
```

Raymond Burr

1. RAYMOND
2. BURR
3. left a MEDIOCRE
4. FILM career
5. for a STELLAR
6. one on TELEVISION.
7. After GUEST
8. PARTS
9. on "The BIGELOW
10. THEATRE,"
11. "DRAGNET,"
12. and "PLAYHOUSE 90,"
13. he BEGAN a
14. NINE
15. YEAR
16. STINT as
17. the EMMY- WINNING
18. PERRY
19. MASON,
20. a CHARACTER he
21. even PLAYED on
22. an EPISODE of
23. "The JACK
24. BENNY Program".
25. LATER,
26. he REPRISED the role
27. in MORE THAN
28. two DOZEN
29. TV MOVIES.
30. He SPENT
31. EIGHT years acting in
32. a WHEELCHAIR
33. as "IRONSIDE,"
34. and HOSTED
35. "UNSOLVED
36. MYSTERIES."

Word-Find 37

```
B R B P L A Y H O U S E S P N
R S E I V O M V T E V D T I A
P U K T E D O S I P E N R S G
D A C X C P E R R Y I O T T E
E R R U B A E E A T N M E E B
S M O T J T R L S S E Y L L A
I N M D S C P A I J I A E L C
R A B Y O T D D H A G R V A G
P H M I W H E E L C H A I R M
E T D Y G I O N V K T E S L A
R E S O V E N S G L B Y I A S
M R P P Z M L N T A O F O T O
U O E M O E I O I E R S N E N
C M N B E N N Y W N D D N R S
E R T A E H T S E U G A O U R
```

"Rawhide"

1. **ADVENTURE**
2. **BLACK** and white
3. Trail **BOSS**
4. Paul **BRINEGAR**
5. Ian **CABOT**
6. **CATTLE** drives
7. **CLAY**
8. **CLINT** Eastwood
9. Jed **COLBY**
10. **COOK**
11. **DANGER**
12. **DROVER**
13. **ERIC** Fleming
14. **HORSES**
15. **HOUR** long
16. John **IRELAND**
17. **JOHN** Ireland
18. **MUSHY**

19. **PETE** Nolan
20. Jim **QUINCE**
21. **RAYMOND** St.
    Jacques
22. **ROWDY**
23. **RUNNERS**
24. Joe **SCARLETT**
25. **SCOUTS**
26. **SIMON** Baker
27. **SOLOMON**
28. Hey **SOOS**
29. **TEAM**
30. **THEME** song
31. **TRAVELS**
32. **WESTERN**
33. **WISHBONE**
34. Sheb **WOOLEY**

```
E R U T N E V D A X U N X X Q
R O E T E P W H M K B M K S Z
R A G E N I R B S T U O C S U
K C O L B Y I N B S D A A O M
G O J R A G R S H U T M L B N
M W O A H E E Y V T J P B Y W
I E I C T S F S L D R O V E R
B R K S R S L E V A R T M L M
D H E O H E I E Y N X H A O S
O W H L R B G M C D O E E O R
C U A O A Y O N H N F M T W E
B L W M S N A N A X I E I C N
T D I O D H D L E D V U I S N
Y P O N T O B A C K F R Q Q U
T S K X T J O C K G E H O U R
```

"Gilmore Girls" Guest Stars

1. (U.S.) SECRETARY
2. of STATE
3. MADELEINE
4. ALBRIGHT
5. COMFORTED
6. RORY in a
7. DREAM.
8. CAROLE
9. KING
10. APPEARED as a
11. MUSIC
12. STORE
13. OWNER.
14. SINGER
15. SEBASTIAN Bach
16. and "THE O.C."
17. star Adam BRODY
18. were LANE'S
19. BANDMATES.
20. (CNN) CORRESPON-DENT
21. CHRISTIANE
22. AMANPOUR,
23. The BANGLES,
24. Seth MACFARLANE,
25. and POLITICIAN
26. BARBARA Levy
27. BOXER
28. all PLAYED
29. THEMSELVES.

```
T N E D N O P S E R R O C C R
K J E N I E L E D A M N O O L
M A E R D P O V Z U T E R M Q
A S E N A L S L P K H Y S F Q
C A P P E A R E D T N I N O M
F H B K A Y O S B L B A H R U
A R R S F E O M X A I R A T S
R R E I E D R E T C S R O E I
L U N G S L S H I C A T T D C
A O W F N T G T S B L A I V Y
N P O V A I I N R T M T Z A G
E N C T R L S A A D O L X T N
H A E B O O B Q N B O R I N I
S M L P M Y R A T E R C E S K
C A R O L E B O X E R C S X Z
```

Liz Torres

1. **ACTRESS**
2. **Liz TORRES**
3. **has MADE**
4. **OVER**
5. **one HUNDRED**
6. **GUEST**
7. **APPEARANCES**
8. **in TV SHOWS.**
9. **She was a**
   REGULAR
10. **on "The FAMOUS**
11. **TEDDY Z,"**
12. **"TEQUILA and**
13. **BONETTI," and**
14. **"The JOHN**
15. **LARROQUETTE**
    Show."
16. **She has**

RECURRING
17. **ROLES on**
18. **"GILMORE**
19. **GIRLS," as**
20. **STARS**
21. **HOLLOW'S**
22. **LOCAL**
23. **DANCE**
24. **INSTRUCTOR,**
25. **MISS**
26. **PATTY, and**
27. **"UGLY BETTY,"**
28. **as EVELYN,**
29. **WILHELMINA**
    Slater's
30. **HOUSEKEEPER.**

Word-Find 40

```
E R O M L I G Q P W C W H S W
T R E S S I M A I M S N O E Y
T A U A I D T L L E A U U R G
E L R D A T H T C I S D S R U
U U S N Y E H N E R U W E O E
Q G C G L Q A K V N O Q K T S
O E L M N R C V E L O L E S T
R R I Y A I V S L S C B E T N
R N K E B I R O Y G T R P S D
A E P G G E H R N V T A E R Z
L P V I N S T R U C T O R D Y
A S R O H H C T A C T J Y S D
O L A C O L N B Y J E C V S D
S V S C J N U H U N D R E D E
W V I F A M O U S W O H S V T
```

Barbra Streisand

1. AFTER
2. APPEARING
3. as a GUEST on
4. "The JUDY
5. GARLAND Show,"
6. BABS did
7. SPECIALS of her own.
8. "MY NAME IS Barbra"
9. won a PEABODY and
10. five EMMYS.
11. "COLOR ME Barbra"
12. was PARTLY
13. FILMED in the
14. PHILADELPHIA
15. MUSEUM of Art.
16. "The BELLE of
17. 14th STREET"
18. FOCUSED on
19. VAUDEVILLE.
20. "(A) HAPPENING
21. in CENTRAL
22. PARK was
23. JUST THAT —
24. an OUTDOOR
25. CONCERT.
26. "Barbra STREISAND...
27. and OTHER
28. MUSICAL
29. INSTRUMENTS"
30. MATCHED
31. her VOICE
32. with EVERY
33. instrument IMAGINABLE.

Word-Find 41

```
K X M D E S U C O F V O I C E
J Y D U J R W O S K T B D B I
B D E X E Y O L C H R N H M A
A O W L R S A O E O A A A D N
M B J E L I U R D S N G P N B
U A V U C I D M I T I C P A P
S E X E S E V E E N U D E L A
I P P D H T R E A E E O N R R
C S C C E T T B D M B J I A T
A S T E S C L H L U E D N G L
L A R T N E C I A R A L G T Y
M T D R E T F A Q T B V L S B
S J M Y N A M E I S Y M M E A
L E A P P E A R I N G E X U B
A I H P L E D A L I H P D G S
```

"Still Standing"

1. ASHLEY Tisdale
2. BILL
3. BONNIE
4. BRIAN
5. CHICAGO
6. CHILDREN
7. Working CLASS
8. DENTAL assistant
9. FAMILY
10. FITZ
11. FOGHAT cover band
12. Jami GRETZ
13. Jennifer IRWIN
14. JAMES Patrick Stuart
15. JOHNNY
16. JUDY
17. Kerri KENNEY
18. KEVIN Nealon
19. LAUREN
20. Aunt LINDA
21. LOUISE
22. MARION
23. MARK Addy
24. MARRIAGE
25. The MILLERS
26. Joel MURRAY
27. Renee OLSTEAD
28. PARENTS
29. PERRY
30. Toilet SALESMAN
31. SALLY Struthers
32. SARCASM
33. SISTER
34. SOLEIL Borda
35. High School SWEETHEARTS
36. TAYLOR Ball
37. TINA

Word-Find 42

```
Y N Y J A M E S U Z N O D S C
D A E T S L O B O F T V W P F
K M A R I O N O A L C E C O Y
E S I U O L T N T Y E L R B E
P E R R Y I O N A T L I A G L
C L G P N G T I H M J I L S H
I A Z A A B H E G I T U M T S
U S N C I R A V O L T L D A A
C H I L D R E N F L W J R Y F
A H W D T K R N Y E F C E L J
C D R S E Z R A T R A N A O B
Z T I F Z N R A M S N D H R I
S I S T E R T Z M E N N I F L
Y N E R U A L A K I N A T X L
U F F M A S A L L Y N I V E K
```

Sizable TV Shows

1. Fat ACTRESS
2. Fat ALBERT
3. Little BEAR
4. The BIGGEST Loser
5. Guy's Big BITE
6. Bear in the Big BLUE House
7. Big BROTHER
8. The Big COMFY Couch
9. (A) Little CURIOUS
10. Little EINSTEINS
11. The Big HOUSE
12. American Dragon: JAKE LONG
13. LIL' BUSH
14. Big LOVE
15. Little LULU
16. My Little MARGIE
17. MEDIUM
18. The Little MERMAID
19. Little House on the PRAIRIE
20. The Little RASCALS
21. ROB AND BIG
22. Strawberry SHORTCAKE
23. SIX FEET Under
24. SMALLVILLE
25. Big SPENDER
26. The THIN MAN
27. So Little TIME
28. TINY Toon Adventure
29. Big TROUBLE
30. WANDA at Large
31. WIDE Angle
32. Small WONDER
33. It's a Big Big WORLD

Word-Find 43

```
S L M R T S E G G I B R O J S
L D U A S I C U R I O U S I Z
M I S L R P H X T B C V X I A
Q A L I U G E E A N X F G D H
O M A N E E I N S T E I N S T
L R C F L K D E D E M A O P Q
P E S S L B A E T E W B L R L
I M A E I D V C D X R B E T U
T A R G V O E I T E K H K R L
M H T D L Y U L S R T G A E I
E D I W L M F U B O O X J B L
M B N N A R O M R U K H W L B
I L Y F M H O B O Y O K S A U
T U Q X S A B W A C T R E S S
B E A R E D N O W V G O T R H
```

Police TV

1. ALIAS
2. BARNABY Jones
3. BOOMTOWN
4. CAGNEY & Lacey
5. The CLOSER
6. COLD CASE
7. COLUMBO
8. The COMMISH
9. COPS
10. CRACKER
11. DEXTER
12. DRAGNET
13. The Rockford FILES
14. HAWAII Five-O
15. HILL Street Blues
16. Close to HOME
17. HOMICIDE: Life on the Streets
18. MAGNUM, P.I.
19. MATLOCK
20. MIAMI Vice
21. Criminal MINDS
22. MONK
23. NCIS
24. NUMBERS
25. NYPD Blue
26. Law & ORDER
27. RENO 911
28. The SHIELD
29. The Mod SQUAD
30. STARSKY & Hutch
31. VEGAS
32. The WIRE
33. WITHOUT a Trace

Word-Find 44

```
T M Y E N G A C O E S D A O Q
E F K N O M H C T E M V O F Z
C B S E E D O R L U E O O W Q
I R R A E M E I E O O Y H O Y
R I A X M K F U S N S H N A Y
W F T I C V B G U I O E T L R
N E S A C D L O C I A H R I F
R H R N Z D B N O P O I E A W
T C A M D A W H N M B L D S D
S O X W R A S H I U T L R B L
D P Y N A A U C W N M O O E E
P S A A G I I Q M G C B W S I
A B P E N D I O S A Z Q E N H
Y U V B E C O L U M B O N R S
K C O L T A M M I A M I N D S
```

"Gossip Girl" Cast

1. GOSSIP
2. GIRL
3. VOICE by
4. KRISTEN
5. BELL.
6. BLAKE
7. LIVELY as
8. SERENA van der
9. WOODSEN.
10. LEIGHTON
11. MEESTER as
12. BLAIR
13. WALDORF.
14. CHACE
15. CRAWFORD as
16. NATE
17. ARCHIBALD.
18. Ed WESTWOCK
19. as CHUCK
20. BASS.
21. PENN
22. BADGLEY as
23. Dan HUMPHREY.
24. TAYLOR
25. MOMSEN as
26. JENNY Humphrey.
27. MATTHEW
28. SETTLE as
29. RUFUS Humphrey.
30. KELLY
31. RUTHERFORD as
32. LILLIAN van der
    Woodsen.
33. JESSICA
34. SZOHR as
35. VANESSA
36. ABRAMS.

Word-Find 45

```
X O T B Z Q C S S A B P L O H
Z Q T A Y L O R V L F N P W V
S W E H T T A M A I J E N N Y
L R C L E C N K N W N S K D I
P I R H I S E E E N F D R G U
R I L S U M W E S T W O C K R
G E S L A C F N S M F O R H H
N E T S I R K O A R O W U D O
J A B S O A C T E K V M F J Z
Y B E D E G N H U C P V U S S
N R L H S E T G I H I Y S E R
A A L X C U M I R B J O T R I
W M T A R P H E N P A T V E A
C S H E U K Y L K E L L Y N L
C C J L I V E L Y E L G D A B
```

Mark Sheppard

1. **Anthony ANTHROS**
2. **"BATTLESTAR Galactica"**
3. **"BIONIC Woman"**
4. **BRITISH**
5. **"The CHRONICLE"**
6. **"(CSI:) CRIME Scene Investigation"**
7. **"CSI:NY"**
8. **DRUMS**
9. **"In the Name of the FATHER"**
10. **"FIREFLY"**
11. **"JAG"**
12. **"LAS VEGAS"**
13. **LIGHT a Big Fire**
14. **LOS ANGELES**
15. **MARRIED**
16. **"MEDIUM"**
17. **"MEGALODON"**
18. **"MONK"**
19. **MUSICIAN**
20. **"The PRACTICE"**
21. **SCHOOL of Fish**
22. **"24" SERIES**
23. **"SOLDIER of Fortune"**
24. **"SPECIAL Unit 2"**
25. **"STAR TREK: Voyager"**
26. **"Cock and Bull STORY"**
27. **TWO SONS**
28. **"UNSTOPPABLE"**
29. **"The X-FILES"**

Word-Find 46

```
O N P E L C I N O R H C T N C
Q O C L Y Q V J C G S T O R Y
K D G B Q L P W B E M I R C E
V O E A U N F H L M E D I U M
B L I P J K B E T P M N I M S
F A Y P N R G H R A O S S H E
C G T O I N G O R I A L R K I
A E M T A I A R B G F O E E R
N M I S L S I I E B Y O H R E
T S O N X E P V C I M H T T S
H L W U D F S E C I T C A R P
R G Q R G A I T C S S S F A Z
O W U A L M D L A I I U A T A
S M Q S O L D I E R A N M S O
S N O S O W T H T S Z L Y Z X
```

"The West Wing" Cast

ACTORS

1. **ALLISON** Janney
2. **BRADLEY** Whitford
3. Dule **HILL**
4. **JANEL** Moloney
5. Jimmy **SMITS**
6. **JOSHUA** Malina
7. Rob **LOWE**
8. **MARTIN** Sheen
9. **MARY** McCormack
10. **MOIRA** Kelly
11. Richard **SCHIFF**
12. **JOHN** Spencer
13. **STOCKARD** Channing

CHARACTERS

1. **C.J. CREGG**
2. Josh **LYMAN**
3. **CHARLIE** Young
4. **DONNA** Moss
5. Matt **SANTOS**
6. **WILL** Bailey
7. Sam **SEABORN**
8. **JOSIAH** Bartlet
9. Kate **HARPER**
10. Mandy **HAMPTON**
11. **TOBY** Ziegler
12. Leo **MCGARRY**
13. **ABBEY** Bartlet

Word-Find 47

```
F S D Y M P M A Z H Y W N P K
D E R J E D L A U M I A J V H
O A A V A L W G R L M U Z T H
N B K M I S D P L Y Y R K C I
N O C S A D J A L W I Y X N L
A R O N S C J C R E G G P H L
U N T O B Y X X H B N G T O B
H O S H T J O S I A H A W J Y
S D C T A U B O K L R E J R H
O S H S I R H M G E B L R N B
J C I Y B M P Q W I A A I Q P
G A F G Z T S E X R G T S E U
P P F Y E B B A R C R D G B T
F N E C N O T P M A H N U A V
T B M X A R I O M J C Z T I Y
```

Damian Lewis

1. "The BAKER"
2. "BAND of Brothers"
3. "Hearts and BONES"
4. "BRIDES"
5. BRITISH
6. "CHROMO-PHOBIA"
7. "COLDITZ"
8. Charlie CREWS
9. "Robinson CRUSOE"
10. "DREAM-CATCHER"
11. ETON College
12. "FIVE Gold Rings"
13. "Life FORCE"
14. GUILDHALL School
15. GUITAR
16. "HAMLET"
17. "KEANE"
18. "LIFE"
19. LONDON
20. "MICKY Love"
21. "NYFES"
22. PIANO
23. "The Forsyte SAGA"
24. "The SITUATION"
25. "SOCCER Aid"
26. "STORM-BREAKER"
27. "WARRIORS"

Word-Find 48

```
R E K A E R B M R O T S P V N
W B R I D E S E V I F A D J Y
E O C B Z J K N G Z P R G K F
C N P O Q A Q O H B E S C A E
M E N H B S I T U A T I O N S
H S O P L H P E M Z M Q A N L
Z N X O B L S C T D O L F R K
D S P M D Y A I F Q W N E A A
P O V O M T D H T O A A A T X
A C T R C L E T D I R C Q I S
F C K H O B E F I L R C Y U P
L E E C A I J H Q U I B E G B
L R E N A E K O S P O U D R R
J U D N O D N O L U R I G O B
Y H S P S W E R C L S O R P B
```

"Crossfire"

1. Bob BECKEL
2. Tom BRADEN
3. CLASH
4. CNN
5. CONFLICT
6. CONSERVATIVE
7. CURRENT
8. DEBATE
9. DESK
10. EVENTS
11. FERRARO
12. GUESTS
13. HEATED
14. ISSUES
15. JAMES Carville
16. Michael KINSLEY
17. LEFT wing
18. LIBERAL
19. LOUD
20. LYNNE Cheney
21. MARY Matalin
22. NEWS
23. Robert NOVAK
24. PARTISAN
25. PAT Buchanan
26. PAUL Begala
27. POLITICS
28. Bill PRESS
29. PUNDITS
30. RIGHT wing
31. Tony SNOW
32. John SUNUNU
33. TALK
34. TOPICS
35. TUCKER Carlson

Word-Find 49

```
J E B D H V T X K K Y W V I P
Z V V E E S C N S Y A P O U C
C I O T X B A M E S C V A N W
P T R A V U A L D R E H O U S
Y A A E W R S T C V R U E N L
Y V R H Y N Q C E E B U S U X
Y R R T I H O N K F I L C S R
N E E K I N T C S E M A J L I
O S F C F S U N E D A R B P G
Z N B L A T A L K T B E P R H
A O I D J P B N O D N B A E T
S C I T I L O P U N D I T S O
T S F V U F I O Y I N L O S F
N E W S G C L L L E K C E B P
L C S T S E U G S P J O J Y K
```

In the TV Kitchen

1. "BAREFOOT Contessa"
2. BOBBY Flay
3. Anthony BOURDAIN
4. "Ace of CAKES"
5. CAT CORA
6. Julia CHILD
7. "Kitchen CONFIDENTIAL"
8. EMERIL Lagasse
9. "FOOD 911"
10. GIADA De Laurentiis
11. "GOOD EATS"
12. "Boy Meets GRILL"
13. "HAVE FORK, Will Travel"
14. "HELL'S Kitchen"
15. "IRON CHEF"
16. MARIO Batali
17. Sara MOULTON
18. "The NAKED Chef"
19. Food NETWORK
20. "NIGELLA Bites"
21. Jamie OLIVER
22. PAULA Deen
23. RACHAEL Ray
24. ROCCO DiSpirito
25. SANDRA Lee
26. "The Next Food Network STAR"
27. "TOP CHEF"
28. TYLER Florence

```
L E A H C A R I H D B V E D P
A M L E W L L I R G Z H M L O
I S T L B A R E F O O T N I Z
T K O L D O O F L X P A R H G
N R P S N Y U I N Z K A V C I
E O C C S O V R R E M Y U Z A
D F H O M E T S D A W X Y L D
I E E E R M T L C A T C O R A
F V F M C A N L U S I S E L R
N A E W E U A E V O S N L N D
O H Z D E R K E T T M E I U N
C B O B B Y I C Y W G P K R A
D O O C C O R L Z I O H W A S
G Y V L R U E L N C I R F H C
P B O A J R A J U S K B K F E
```

TV GUIDE

Top Animated TV Shows

1. **AMERICAN Dad!**
2. **ANIMANIACS**
3. **AVATAR: The Last Airbender**
4. **The BACKYARDI-GANS**
5. **BLEACH**
6. **CHOWDER**
7. **DEXTER'S Laboratory**
8. **DIGIMON: Digital Monsters**
9. **DRAGON Ball**
10. **DRAWN Together**
11. **The FAIRLY Odd Parents**
12. **FAMILY Guy**
13. **The FLINTSTONES**
14. **FUTURAMA**
15. **INUYASHA**
16. **Total Drama ISLAND**
17. **Tom and JERRY**
18. **JUSTICE League**
19. **KING of the Hill**
20. **NARUTO**
21. **Danny PHANTOM**
22. **PHINEAS and Ferb**
23. **ROBOT Chicken**
24. **RUGRATS**
25. **SAILOR Moon**
26. **The SIMPSONS**
27. **SOUTH Park**
28. **SUPERMAN**
29. **TOTALLY Spies**
30. **WINX CLUB**
31. **W.I.T.C.H.**
32. **X-MEN**
33. **YU-GI-OH!**

```
R E D W O H C X H O I G U Y P
A H Y E F F B X R Y T S A H I
B V N L X Y V U R O U U I Y S
T A A H L T L R L P L N R T L
O Q C T E A E I E C E I A A A
B S I K A J T R M A X R A X N
O L R N Y R M O S A G N N S D
R E E A M A R U T U F O I O R
U M M A N B R Q R A G M M W A
X O A P C T G D I N P I A I G
H T U O S H K R I S P G N T O
Z N W A R D L K O G E I I C N
D A H S A Y U N I F A D A H T
D H S N J U S T I C E N C G Q
J P F L I N T S T O N E S C Z
```

"Gunsmoke" Season 5 Episodes

1. Belle's BACK
2. BIG Tom
3. The BOOTS
4. BOX O'ROCKS
5. CHERRY Red
6. COLLEEN So Green
7. CROWBAIT Bob
8. Unwanted DEPUTY
9. The DESERTER
10. The EX-URBANITES
11. FALSE Witness
12. GENTLEMEN'S Disagreement
13. GROAT'S Grudge
14. HINKA Do
15. HORSE Deal
16. Kitty's INJURY
17. I THEE Wed
18. Jailbait JANET
19. JOHNNY Red
20. Doc JUDGE
21. KANGAROO
22. KITTY'S Killing
23. MIGUEL'S Daughter
24. MOO MOO Raid
25. Annie OAKLEY
26. ODD MAN Out
27. SALUDOS
28. SPEAK Me Fair
29. TARGET
30. THICK 'n' Thin
31. The TRAGEDIAN
32. Brother WHELP
33. WHERE'D They Go
34. Tag, YOU'RE It

Word-Find 52

```
G K G S V J R H W B D T U Y R
J A N E T O C K I H I E Q E T
S E C T S H A R C N E G T O E
B P B I K N V X O T K R D R Q
O S W N G N E Z L W E A E O Q
X B Y A G Y Q M L S B T B D B
O R R B T R A G E D I A N K S
R O U R M E I D E L K C I H T
O W J U N T S J N C T T T T O
C H N X H A U L A E T N Y S O
K E I E L D M B A Y S E E U B
S L E U G I M D S F L R C G D
A P D E P U T Y D K U Q O H L
M O O M O O P N A O C E H H Z
S T A O R G M O Y R R E H C V
```

TV GUIDE

"Blossom"

1. ANTHONY

2. BLOSSOM

3. Two BROTHERS

4. CATCH phrase

5. CELEBRITY guest stars

6. FAMILY

7. FANTASY scenes

8. FIVE seasons

9. Best FRIEND

10. FUNKY clothing

11. HATS

12. JENNA von Oy

13. JOEY

14. Joey LAWRENCE

15. MAYIM Bialik

16. MICHAEL

Stoyanov

17. Addressed MORAL issues

18. MOTHER left

19. MUSICIAN

20. "My OPINIONATION"

21. The RUSSOS

22. SINGLE parent

23. SIX

24. Very SPECIAL episodes

25. Fast TALKER

26. TEENAGE life

27. Ted WASS

28. "WHOA!"

```
E N I Y H N J B J Y G K V D B
X U E C T S A R T T M Y E O J
L D T R U S S O S N Q O Q F M
N A F L V A R T H K Z A R O X
C O W P E W M H O W R I S A M
Y T I R B E L E C T E S S O L
S A A T E K D R Y N O H T N A
A L H N A N L S D L M H A F M
T K F L N N C E B Q E D H U J
N E D A F E O E A R L U S N H
A R B I M V J I I H B I X K U
F R V C Y I Y F N Q C I W Y B
I E W E Q E L G N I S I Q I F
T Y Q P Q M I Y A M P L M D N
V T W S E G A N E E T O P A X
```

"Playhouse 90"

1. "PLAYHOUSE 90"
2. was a 90-MINUTE
3. ANTHOLOGY
4. DRAMA
5. SERIES that was
6. LIVE, with a
7. TAPED show
8. EVERY
9. FOURTH
10. THURSDAY to give the
11. CAST and
12. CREW a break.
13. The show had both ORIGINAL
14. and ADAPTED
15. STORIES
16. INCLUDING:
17. "REQUIEM for a
18. HEAVY-WEIGHT,"
19. "ELOISE,"
20. "The MIRACLE
21. WORKER,"
22. "The COMEDIAN,"
23. "CHARLEY'S
24. AUNT,"
25. "The HELEN
26. MORGAN
27. STORY,"
28. "The GREAT
29. GATSBY,"
30. "The DAYS
31. of WINE
32. and ROSES,"
33. "JUDGMENT
34. at NUREMBERG,"
35. and "ALAS,
36. BABYLON."

Word-Find 54

```
N A G R O M L Y R O T S Y D F
M D M Y P U E W O R K E R E G
I T A A Q V M V Y H K I C P I
U J Y Y R L A N I G I R O A Y
T H U R S D A Y R L H O M T B
N H A D A P T E D Q B T E R S
U A G E G Z B A L A S S D E T
A Z N I K M P W B C C C I Q A
F W I T E C E Y X H A R A U G
I O D R H W L N A S E R N I M
W L U E O O Y R T S W A I E I
W N L R N S L V I J M E V M N
I E C N T E E O A T A E R G U
N I N F Y H L S G E R C S C T
E V I S U E P L A Y H O U S E
```

Makeovers on TV

1. **AMBUSH Makeover**
2. **BEAUTY and the GeeK**
3. **CELEBRITY Fit Club**
4. **CLEAN House**
5. Style **COURT**
6. **DESERVING Design**
7. **DESIGNED to Sell**
8. **DRESS My Nest**
9. Extreme Makeover: Home **EDITION**
10. **EXTREME Makeover**
11. The Look **FOR LESS**
12. How to Look **GOOD Naked**
13. Get **GORGEOUS**
14. **GROOMED**
15. How Do I **LOOK?**
16. **I WANT a Famous Face**
17. The Biggest **LOSER**
18. **MADE**
19. **MOVIE & a Makeover**
20. Pimp **MY RIDE**
21. America's **NEXT TOP Model**
22. Queer Eye for the **STRAIGHT Guy**
23. The **SWAN**
24. **TRADING Spaces**
25. What Not to **WEAR**

```
E N O F M T O J S S T O U Y M
D B E C K P N F W X R H G T D
A E N X M L E A N G U H O I K
M A M B T D N A W N O E R R B
J U N O I T E U L I C A G B K
V T J T O L O S C D W X E E B
O Y I E C R H P E A K E O L D
G O C X T H G I A R T S U E G
N D R E S S T Q L T V E S C L
A W W U Y W E A R N M I L E E
O O B O M Y R I D E G L N F B
J M G E I V O M R N S O X G V
A Q W B W M V T E U Y O O N G
K R A Y D N X D S N N K L D D
N F O R L E S S C V F Q B Q E
```

Shows by the Numbers

1. Car 54, Where ARE YOU?
2. BABYLON 5
3. BEN 10
4. BEVERLY Hills, 90210
5. CATCH 21
6. CLASS of 3000
7. The 700 CLUB
8. Three's COMPANY
9. Eight Is ENOUGH
10. FIRST 48
11. Two and a HALF MEN
12. 7th HEAVEN
13. 48 HOURS
14. JAKE 2.0
15. JUST the Ten of Us
16. Two of a KIND
17. NANNY 911
18. NINE TO FIVE
19. ODYSSEY 5
20. ONE LIFE to Live
21. ONE TREE Hill
22. POWER of 10
23. The $25,000 PYRAMID
24. RESCUE 911
25. RIN TIN TIN (K-9) Cop
26. 30 ROCK
27. SEALAB 2020
28. 21 Jump STREET
29. STUDIO 60 on the Sunset Strip
30. My SUPER Sweet 16
31. THE NINE
32. 3rd Rock from THE SUN
33. One Day at a TIME
34. TWO GUYS and a Girl
35. Six Feet UNDER
36. Eights Days a WEEK
37. ZOEY 101
38. 64 ZOO LANE

```
V L U W H H V H O U R S R S G
T Y N N A N U S E H T C E S Y
H Z C E E E Q N T R N K W A W
K J O N T M P R E P U S O L W
I X M O R F I E N B I D P C Y
N O P U L L T T Q O Y E O Z L
D I A G B A L A E S L L S T R
T R N H K H N H S P T Y S W E
U H Y E C V E E Y U U U B Z V
O G E T T A Y R U G J U D A E
Y W A N V O A F O C L N C I B
E C W E I M F W I C S D H T O
R I N T I N T I N R K E K A J
A N H D O Y E G V F S R R P N
L B O N E L I F E E R T E N O
```

"Desperate Housewives" Names

1. ANDREW Van de Kamp
2. Matthew APPLEWHITE
3. AUSTIN McCann
4. BETTY Applewhite
5. BREE Hodge
6. CALEB Applewhite
7. CARLOS Solis
8. DANIELLE Van de Kamp
9. DYLAN Mayfair
10. EDIE Britt
11. GABRIELLE Solis
12. GEORGE Williams
13. JULIE Mayer
14. KARL Mayer
15. KATHERINE Mayfair
16. KAYLA Scavo
17. LYNETTE Scavo
18. MARY ALICE Young
19. MIKE Delfino
20. ORSON Hodge
21. PARKER Scavo
22. PAUL Young
23. PORTER Scavo
24. PRESTON Scavo
25. John ROWLAND
26. Tom SCAVO
27. SUSAN Delfino
28. Rex VAN DE KAMP
29. ZACH Young

```
M M K G M O O E N A S U S E F
C H L C J V V I V C M H O O I
V E P M A K E D N A V L L O V
E I K C X P K E R D I K R F Z
V L S A N P P Y R N S A A A W
R U L R Y O A L Z A F T C K K
O J Y E L L T U E L S H N L G
A U S T I N A S L W D E W T G
S X G C T R R S E O H R S T E
B K E J P E B T H R E I A T O
C B W P E O B A V T P N T R R
A P A R K E R K G P D E S E G
L A B E K I M T O R N O T C E
E L L E I N A D E Y N A L Y D
B B C O Z U C W L R H P S H E
```

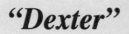

1. ADOPTED
2. Blood spatter ANALYSIS
3. ANGEL
4. Jennifer CARPENTER
5. CRIME scenes
6. C. S. LEE
7. DARK comedy
8. DAVID Zayas
9. DEBORAH
10. DETECTIVE
11. DEXTER Morgan
12. "Darkly DREAMING Dexter"
13. Two EMMYS
14. ERIK King
15. FATHER
16. HARRY
17. "The ICE TRUCK Killer"
18. JULIE Benz
19. LAUREN Velez
20. LT. LAGUERTA
21. MIAMI
22. MICHAEL (C.) Hall
23. Based on NOVEL
24. POLICE department
25. James REMAR
26. RITA
27. SECRET life
28. SERIAL killer
29. SGT. DOAKES
30. SHOWTIME
31. SOCIOPATH
32. VIGILANTE
33. VINCE

Word-Find 58

```
I G T Z D L H E R I K U R C P
J N J E O A A B Y X F R S N F
W I F U R E M I R C H L A A Z
O M P O L I C E R T E V Q D Q
X A B N M I C H A E L I V O C
R E H T A F E P H R S G M P L
D R S E K A O D T G S I Z T E
D D E I V I N C E E A L L E V
P E Q T C I L O M M L A B D O
T M X O N E T I I A G N G A N
E M S T G E T C U U R T B V K
R Y R N E W P R E K V E T I L
C S A I O R E R U T I G M D M
E N I H T N T N A C E V K A G
S I S Y L A N A H C K D J N R
```

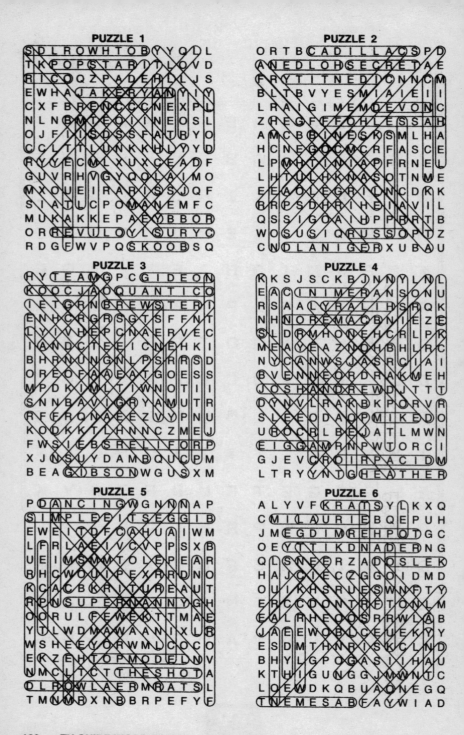

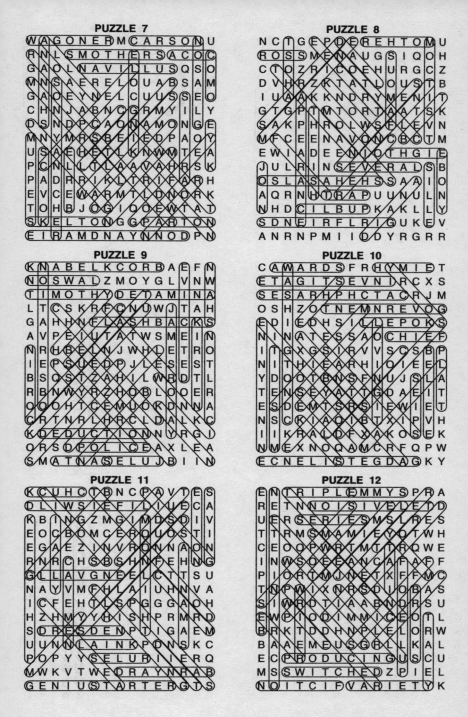

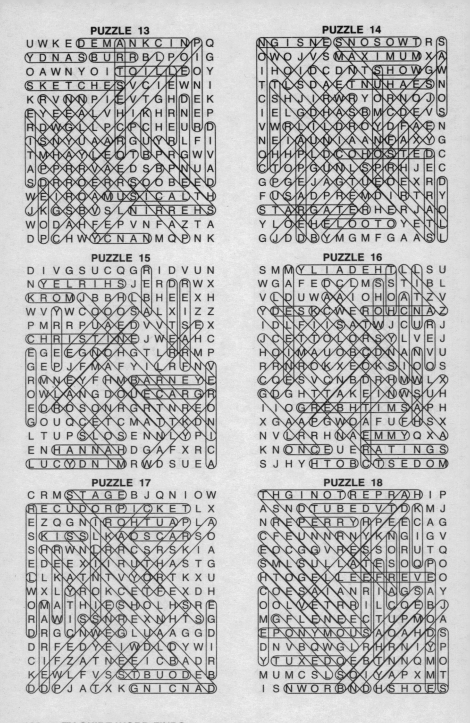

PUZZLE 13

PUZZLE 14

PUZZLE 15

PUZZLE 16

PUZZLE 17

PUZZLE 18

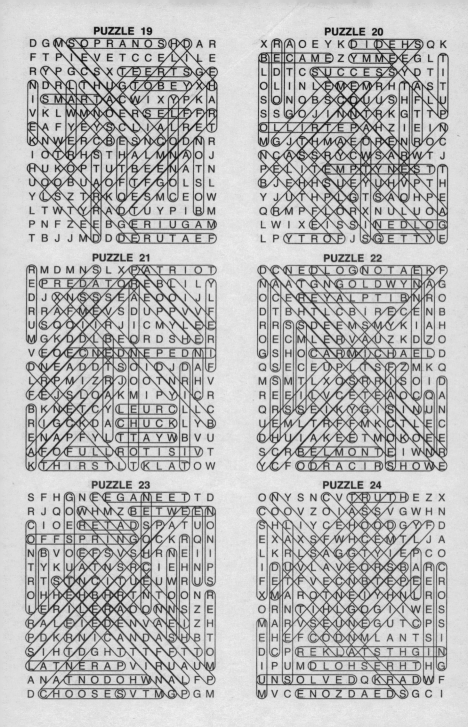

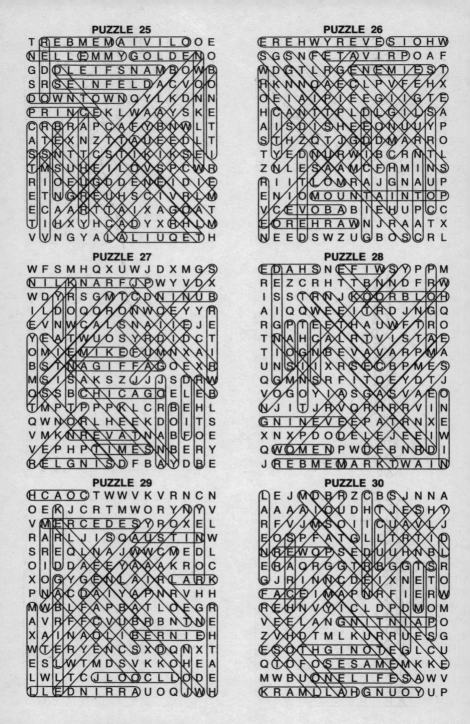

PUZZLE 25

```
T R E B M E M A I V I L O O E
N E L L E M M Y G O L D E N O
G D O L E I F S N A M B O W B
S R S E I N F E L D A C V O O
O O W N T O W N Q Y L K D N N
P R I N C E K L W A A Y S K E
C R B R A P C A F Y B N W L T
A T E X N Z T T A U E E D L T
S S N T T C S T X I K S E I
T M S U H E I L O V S P C W R
R I O E U G O D E N E I D I E
E T N G R E U H S C I V R L M
E C A A R T T A I X A G O A T
T I H X Y H C A D Y X R H L M
V V N G Y A L A L I U Q E T H
```

PUZZLE 26

```
E R E H W Y R E V E S I O H W
S G S N F E T A V I R P O A F
W D G T L R G E N E M I E S T
H K N N O A E C L P V F E H X
O E I A I P I E E G I X G T E
H C A N T T P L D L G I L S A
A I S D I S H E E O N U U Y P
S T H Z Q T J G D D M A R R O
T Y E D N U R W I B C R N T L
Z N L E S A A M C F A M I N S
R I I T L O M R A J G N A U P
E N I O M O U N T A I N T O P
V C E V O B A B I E H U P C C
E O R E H R A W N J R A A T X
N E E D S W Z U G B O S C R L
```

PUZZLE 27

```
W F S M H Q X U W J D X M G S
N I L K N A R F J P W Y V D X
W D Y R S G M T C D N I N U B
I L D O Q O R O N W O E Y Y R
E V N W C A L S N A I I E J E
Y E A T W U O S Y R D I D C T
O M I E M I K E F U M N X A I
B S T N A G I F F A G O E X R
M S I S A K S Z J J J S D R W
O S S B C H I C A G O E L E B
T M P T P P P K L C R B E H L
Q W N O R L H E E K D O I T S
V M K N R E V A T N A B F O E
V E P H P T I M E S N B E R Y
R E L G N I S D F B A Y D B E
```

PUZZLE 28

```
E D A H S N E F I W S Y P P M
R E Z C R H T T B N N D F R W
I S S T R N J K O O R B L O H
A I Q Q W E E I T R D J N G Q
R G P T E E T H A U W F T R O
T N A H C A L R T V I S T A E
T I O G N B E V A V A R P M A
U N S I I X R S E C B P M E S
Q G M N S R F I T O E Y D T J
V O G O Y I A S G A S V A E O
N J I T J R V O R H R R V I N
G N I N E V E E P A T R N X E
X N X P D O D E L E J E E I W
Q W O M E N P W O E B N R D I
J R E B M E M A R K T W A I N
```

PUZZLE 29

```
H C A O C T W W V K V R N C N
O E K J C R T M W O R Y N Y V
V M E R C E D E S Y R O X E L
R A R L J I S O A U S T I N W
S R E Q L N A J W W C M E D L
O I D D A E E Y A A A K R O C
X O G Y G E N L A I R L A R K
P N A C D A I Y A P N R V H H
M W B L F A P B A T L O E G R
A V R F F C V U B B N T N E
X A I N A O L I B E R N I E H
W T E R Y E N C S X D Q N X T
E S L W T M D S V K K O H E A
L W L T C J L O O C L L O D E
U L E D N I R R A U O Q J W H
```

PUZZLE 30

```
L E J M O B R Z C B S J N N A
A A A A X O U D H T J E S H Y
R F V J M S O I I C U A V L J
E O S P F A T G L L T R T I D
N R E W O P S E D U U H N B L
E R A O R G G T B B G G T S R
G J R I N N C D E I X N E T O
F A C E I M A P N R F I E R W
R E H N V Y I C L D P D M O M
V E E L A N G N I T N I A P O
Z V H D T M L K U R R U E S G
E S O T H G I N O T E G L C U
Q T O F O S E S A M E M K K E
M W B U O N E L I F E S A W V
K R A M L L A H G N U O Y U P
```

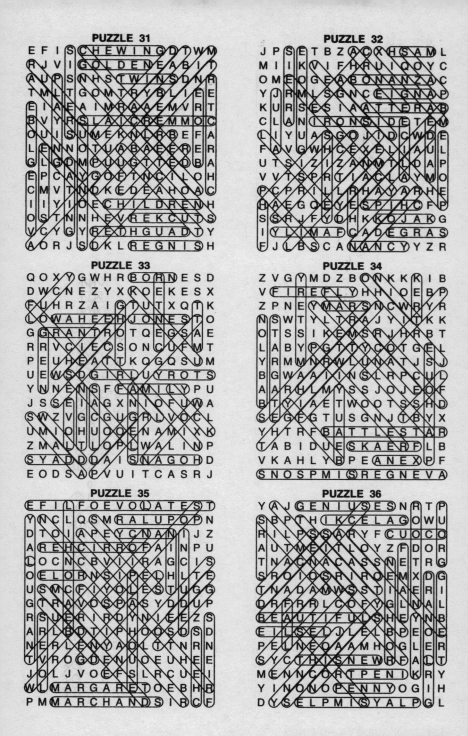

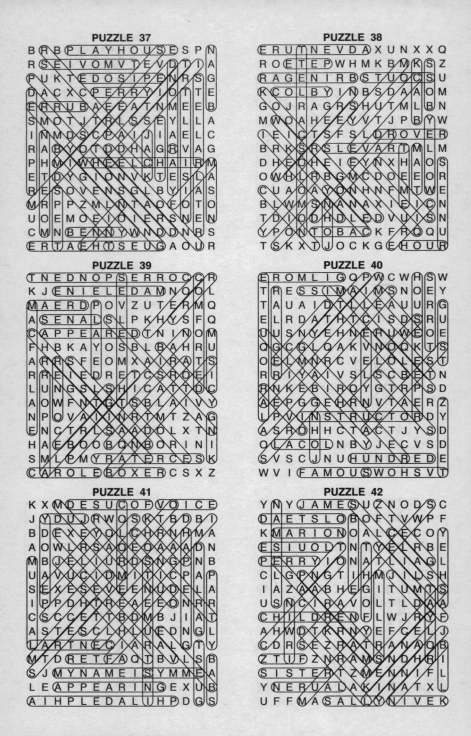

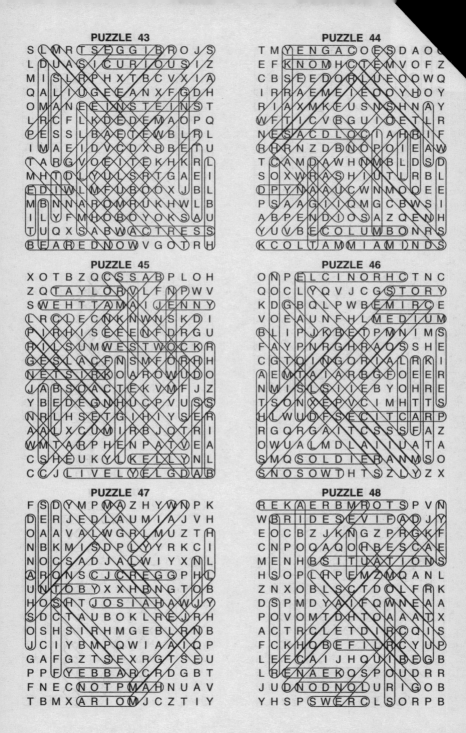

PUZZLE 43

```
S L M R T S E G G I B R O J S
L D U A S I C U R I O U S I Z
M I S L R P H X T B C V X I A
Q A L I U G E E A N X F G D H
O M A N E E I N S T E I N S T
L R C F L K D E D E M A O P Q
P E S S L B A E T E W B L R L
I M A E I D V C D X B B E T U
T A R G V O E I T E K H K R L
M H T D L Y U L S R T G A E I
E D I W L M F U B O O X J B L
M B N N A R O M R U K H W L B
I L Y F M H O B O Y O K S A U
T U Q X S A B W A C T R E S S
B E A R E D N O W V G O T R H
```

PUZZLE 44

```
T M Y E N G A C O E S D A O G
E F K N O M H C T E M V O F Z
C B S E E D O R L U E O O W Q
I R R A E M E I E O O Y H O Y
R I A X M K E U S N S H N A Y
W F T I C V B G U I O E T L R
N E S A C D L O C I A H R I F
R H R N Z D B N O P O I E A W
T C A M D A W H N M B L D S D
S O X W R A S H I U T L R B L
D P Y N A A U C W N M O O E E
P S A A G I I Q M G C B W S I
A B P E N D I O S A Z Q E N H
Y U V B E C O L U M B O N R S
K C O L T A M M I A M I N D S
```

PUZZLE 45

```
X O T B Z Q C S S A B P L O H
Z Q T A Y L O R V L F N P W V
S W E H T T A M A I J E N N Y
L R C L E C N K N W N S K D I
P I R H I S E E N F D R G U
R I L S U M W E S T W O C K R
G E S L A C F N S M F O R H H
N E X S I R K O A R O W U D O
J A B S O A C T E K V M F J Z
Y B E D E G N H U C P V U S S
N R L H S E T G I H I Y S E R
A A L X C U M I R B J O T R I
W M T A R P H E N P A T V E A
C S H E U K Y L K E L L Y N L
C C J L I V E L Y E L G D A B
```

PUZZLE 46

```
O N P E L C I N O R H C T N C
Q O C L Y Q V J C G S T O R Y
K D G B Q L P W B E M I R C E
V O E A U N F H L M E D I U M
B L I P J K B E T P M N I M S
F A Y P N R G H R A O S H E
C G T O I N G O R I A L R K I
A E M T A I A R B G E O E E R
N M I S L S I I E B Y O H R E
T S O N X E P V C I M H T T S
H L W U D F S E C I T C A R P
R G O R G A I T C S S S F A Z
O W U A L M D L A I I U A T A
S M Q S O L D I E R A M M S O
S N O S O W T H T S Z L Y Z X
```

PUZZLE 47

```
F S D Y M P M A Z H Y W N P K
D E R J E D L A U M I A J V H
O A A V A L W G R L M U Z T H
N B K M I S D P L Y Y R K C I
N O C S A D J A L W I Y X N L
A R O N S C J C R E G G P H L
U N T O B Y X X H B N G T O B
H O S R T J O S I A H A W J Y
S D C T A U B O K L R E J R H
O S H S I R H M G E B L R N B
J C I Y B M P Q W I A A I Q P
G A F G Z T S E X R G T S E U
P P F Y E B B A R C R D G B T
F N E C N O T P M A H N U A V
T B M X A R I O M J C Z T I Y
```

PUZZLE 48

```
R E K A E R B M R O T S P V N
W B R I D E S E V I P A D J Y
E O C B Z J K N G Z P R G K F
C N P O Q A Q O R B E S C A E
M E N H B S I T U A T I O N S
H S O P L A P E M Z M Q A N L
Z N X O B L S C T D O L F R K
D S P M D Y A I F Q W N E A A
P O V O M T D H T O A A A T X
A C T R C L E T D I R C Q I S
F C K H O B E F I L R C Y U P
L E E C A I J H O U I B E G B
L R E N A E K O S P O U D R R
J U D N O D N O L U R I G O B
Y H S P S W E R C L S O R P B
```

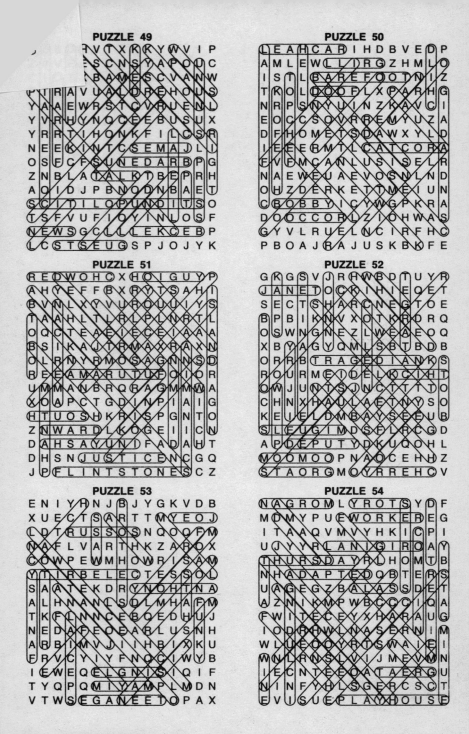

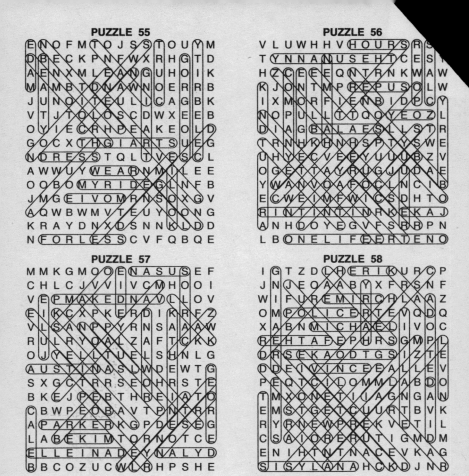

PUZZLE 55

```
E N O F M T O J S S T O U Y M
D B E C K P N F W X R H G T D
A E N X M L E A N G U H O I K
M A M B T O N A W N O E R R B
J U N O X I T E U L I C A G B K
V T J T O L O S C D W X E E B
O Y I E C R H P E A K E O L D
G O C X T H G I A R T S U E G
N O R E S S T Q L T V E S C L
A W W U Y W E A R N M I L E E
O O B O M Y R I D E G L N F B
J M G E I V O M R N S O X G V
A Q W B W M V T E U Y O O N G
K R A Y D N X D S N N K L D D
N F O R L E S S C V F Q B Q E
```

PUZZLE 56

```
V L U W H H V H O U R S R S
T Y N N A N U S E H T C E S T
H Z C E E E Q N T R N K M A W
K J O N T M P R E X P U S O L W
I X M O R F I X E N B I D P C Y
N O P U L L T T Q O Y E O Z L
D I A G B A L A E S L L S T R
T R N H K O N D S P T Y S W E
U H Y E C V E E Y U U B Z V
O G E T T A Y R U G J U D A E
Y W A N V O A F O C L N C I B
E C W E X I M F W I C S D H T O
R I N T X N T X N R K E K A J
A N H O O Y E G V F S B B P N
L B O N E L I F E E R T E N O
```

PUZZLE 57

```
M M K G M O O E N A S U S E F
C H L C J V V I V C M H O O I
V E P M A K E D N A V L L O V
E I K C X P K E R D I K R F Z
V L S A N P P Y R N S A A A W
R U L R Y O A L Z A F T C K K
O J Y E L L T U E L S H N L G
A U S T X X N A S L W D E W T G
S X G C X T R R S E O H R S T E
B K E J P E B T H R E I A T O
C B W P E O B A V T P N T R R
A P A R K E R K G P D E S E G
L A B E K I M T O R N O T C E
E L L E I N A D E Y N A L Y D
B B C O Z U C W L R H P S H E
```

PUZZLE 58

```
I G T Z D L H E R I K U R C P
J N J E O A A B Y X F R S N F
W I F U R E M I R C H L A A Z
O M P O X L I C E R T E V Q D Q
X A B N M I C H A E L I V O C
R E H T A F E P H R S G M P L
O R S E K A O D T G S I Z T E
O D E I V I N C E E A L L E V
P E Q T X I D O M M D A B D O
T M X O N E X T I I A G N G A N
E M S T G E T C U U R T B V K
R Y R N E W P R E X K V E T I L
C S A I O B E R U T I G M D M
E N I H T N T N A C E V K A G
S I S Y L A N A H C K D J N B
```